ELECTRONIC JOB SEARCH

ALMANAC 2000

ADAMS

ELECTRONIC JOB SEARCH

ALMANAC 2000

Steven Graber, *Managing Editor*
Thomas F. Blackett, *Editor*
Heidi E. Sampson, *Researcher/Editor*

Adams Media Corporation
Holbrook, Massachusetts

Published by Adams Media Corporation
260 Center Street, Holbrook, Massachusetts 02343

ISBN: 1-58062-221-6
ISSN: 1099-016X
Manufactured in Canada.

J I H G F E D C B A

Product or brand names used in this book may be trademarks or registered
trademarks. Any use of these names does not convey endorsement by or other
affiliation with the name holder.

Adams Media Corporation, a publisher of career books and software
products, owns CareerCity, a career-related site on the World Wide Web. While
the publisher is a potential competitor with many of the services and products
listed in this book, every effort has been made to ensure editorial objectivity and
impartiality.

Every effort has been made to ensure that all material in this book is current
as of the time of this writing. However, due to the nature of the technologies
discussed here, this information is subject to change. Readers should check with
the individual services and products to find up-to-date information, such as current
prices, fees, and features.

This publication is designed to provide accurate and authoritative information with
regard to the subject matter covered. It is sold with the understanding that the
publisher is not engaged in rendering legal, accounting, or other professional advice. If
legal advice or other expert assistance is required, the services of a qualified
professional person should be sought.

— From a *Declaration of Principles* jointly adopted by a Committee of the
American Bar Association and a Committee of Publishers and Associations.

This book is available at quantity discounts for bulk purchases.
For more information, call 1-800-872-5627 (in Massachusetts 781-767-8100) or
email at jobbank@adamsonline.com.

Visit our home page at http://www.careercity.com

CONTENTS

Top career publications from Adams Media Corporation

Other Adams Almanacs:

The Adams Cover Letter Almanac ($12.95)
The Adams Executive Recruiters Almanac
  ($16.95)
The Adams Job Interview Almanac ($12.95)
The Adams Jobs Almanac, 2000 ($16.95)
The Adams Resume Almanac ($10.95)

Other Career Titles:

Cold Calling Techniques, 3rd Ed. ($8.95)
College Grad Job Hunter, 4th Ed. ($14.95)
Complete Resume & Job Search Book for
  College Students ($12.95)
Cover Letters That Knock 'em Dead
  ($10.95)
Every Woman's Essential Job Hunting &
  Resume Book ($10.95)
How to Become Successfully Self-
  Employed, 2nd Ed. ($9.95)
Knock 'em Dead, 2000 ($12.95)
The New Rules of the Job Search Game
  ($10.95)
Outplace Yourself ($15.95)
Over 40 and Looking for Work? ($7.95)
The Resume Handbook, 3rd Ed. ($7.95)
Resumes That Knock 'em Dead ($10.95)
The 250 Job Interview Questions You'll
  Most Likely Be Asked ($9.95)

The JobBank Series:
each JobBank book is $16.95

The Atlanta JobBank, 2000
The Austin/San Antonio JobBank, 2nd Ed.
The Boston JobBank, 2000
The Carolina JobBank, 6th Ed.
The Chicago JobBank, 2000
The Connecticut JobBank, 1st Ed.
The Dallas-Fort Worth JobBank, 2000
The Denver JobBank, 11th Ed.
The Detroit JobBank, 9th Ed.

The Florida JobBank, 2000
The Houston JobBank, 10th Ed.
The Indiana JobBank, 2nd Ed.
The Las Vegas JobBank, 2nd Ed.
The Los Angeles JobBank, 2000
The Minneapolis-St. Paul JobBank, 11th Ed.
The Missouri JobBank, 2nd Ed.
The Northern New England JobBank, 1st Ed.
The New Jersey JobBank, 1st Ed.
The New Mexico JobBank, 1st Ed.
The Metropolitan New York JobBank, 2000
The Upstate New York JobBank, 1st Ed.
The Ohio JobBank, 10th Ed.
The Greater Philadelphia JobBank, 2000
The Phoenix JobBank, 8th Ed.
The Pittsburgh JobBank, 2nd Ed.
The Portland JobBank, 2nd Ed.
The Salt Lake City JobBank, 1st Ed.
The San Francisco Bay Area JobBank, 2000
The Seattle JobBank, 2000
The Tennessee JobBank, 4th Ed.
The Virginia JobBank, 3rd Ed.
The Metropolitan Washington DC JobBank,
  2000
The Wisconsin JobBank, 1st Ed.

The JobBank Guide to Computer &
  High-Tech Companies, 2nd Ed.
  ($17.95)

The JobBank Guide to Health Care
  Companies, 1st Ed. ($16.95)

The National JobBank, 2000
  (Covers entire U.S.: $370.00 hc --
  standing order prices are
  also available)

The JobBank Guide to Employment
  Services, 2000-2001(Covers entire
  U.S.: $230.00 hc -- standing order
  prices are also available)

If you cannot find these titles at your favorite book outlet,
you may order them directly from the publisher.

BY PHONE: Call 800/872-5627 (in Massachusetts 781/767-8100).
We accept Visa, Mastercard, and American Express. $4.95 will be added for S&H.
BY MAIL: Write out the full titles of the books you'd like to order and send payment,
including $4.95 for S&H to: Adams Media Corporation, 260 Center Street, Holbrook MA
02343 U.S.A.
BY FAX: 800/872-5628.
BY E-MAIL: jobbank@adamsonline.com
30-day money back guarantee.
All books available on standing order.

--VISIT OUR WEBSITE--
http://www.careercity.com

ACKNOWLEDGMENTS

Special thanks go to Chris Maligno, Scott Masson, and Bill Duffy for all of their technical assistance, patience, and helpful suggestions and information. Additional thanks go to Sue Beale for generously offering her skills and time regarding the layout and design of this book, and to Chris Ciaschini for his assistance with designing the cover.

Thanks also go to Liz Kane, Cathy Kasey, and Mary Susi for their assistance in conducting a tremendous amount of World Wide Web research.

HOW TO USE
THIS BOOK

The *Adams Electronic Job Search Almanac 2000* is designed to prepare you to find a job today, in this, the information age. In here, you will find hundreds of electronic resources to help with every aspect of your job hunt, from preparing your resume and finding job openings to preparing for electronic job interviews. Regardless of your level of experience with technology, you will find an abundance of valuable information within these pages.

You can approach this book in two different ways. One option is to read it cover to cover so that you learn about the full spectrum of electronic job hunting possibilities. Or, you can use it as a handy reference guide in order to find resources of particular interest, such as the Web address for a job hunting site that specializes in health care jobs.

In our **Introduction**, we focus on the overall concept of electronic job hunting. This includes a discussion of *why* it's important to keep up with changing technology trends impacting your job search, and an overview of how to get started—including hardware and software, setting up, and strategies to follow.

You may decide to begin your electronic job hunt by creating an electronic resume. In **Chapter One**, you'll learn why you should have one, and where to distribute it in order to maximize your exposure. We also tell you about multimedia and video resumes—two unusual types of electronic resumes—that are sure to make you stand out with certain employers.

But if you simply want to know where to find job openings online, turn to **Chapters Two** through **Five**. In these chapters, we tell you about the *best* places to look for jobs. You'll discover where to find millions of job listings online through the World Wide Web, commercial online services, Usenet, and more.

You'll also learn how to create a target list of potential employers, and where to uncover valuable company information that you can use during your interview. And if you're interested in finding the best online discussion groups for meeting and chatting with other professionals in your field, turn to our chapter on networking. You'll find all this information and more in **Chapters Six**, **Seven**, and **Eight**.

Finally, **Chapter Nine** covers other aspects of electronic job hunting, including commercial career and job-search software products, and what to do if you're told you'll talk to a computer, instead of a person, at your next job interview.

About the Update

Keep in mind that, in this age of rapidly changing technology, electronic resources are coming and going faster than you can say "information superhighway." Since publication of the 1999 edition of this book, we have watched once powerful companies and services disappear and new players emerge to take their place, while other sites have merged to form mega sites.

We have made our best efforts to ensure that the information in this book is as accurate and up-to-date as possible, verifying every shred of information from the last edition, deleting the information that was outdated or no longer useful, while adding lots of new resources for jobseekers and employers alike. That said, there is little doubt that some changes will occur even in the time it takes for this book to be printed, and information, particularly concerning prices, should be used more as a guideline than as gospel.

Understanding the Listings

Commercial Online Services

In these listings, you will usually find the name of the resource, followed by the **Keyword** that's necessary in order to access the resource. Each service calls its keyword something different. In America Online, it's "keyword"; and in CompuServe and The

Microsoft Network, it's "go." The **Number of job listings** is rounded down; for instance, if a site had 503 job listings, we said 500; if a site had 7,128 listings, we rounded that down to 7,100. **Types of jobs** indicates in general terms what fields or job categories you are likely to find job listings for; similarly, **Locations of jobs** indicates for what countries, states, or cities job listings can be found. **Frequency of updates** indicates how often job listings are added to the database. **Search criteria available** shows you how the database can be searched. Most sites allow you to search by some combination of job category, location, company, or keywords; some let you search only by keyword. And the **Insider tips** section is a general overview of a service and its special features, along with helpful tips for the insider. **Note:** When we were unable to determine information with a reasonable degree of accuracy, N/A was used.

Gopher

In the Gopher listings, you will find the name of the site, followed by its address. The **Number of job listings** is rounded down; for instance, if a site had 503 job listings, we said 500; if a site had 11,128 listings, we rounded that down to 11,100. **Types of jobs** indicates in general terms what fields or job categories you are likely to find job listings for; similarly, **Locations of jobs** indicates for what countries, states, or cities job listings can be found. **Frequency of updates** indicates how often job listings are added to the database. **Search criteria available** shows you how the database can be searched by job category, location, company, or keywords. **Key features** discusses other career resources, besides job listings, available on the site. And **Insider tips** gives our impression of a given site and its resources. **Note:** When we were unable to determine information with a reasonable degree of accuracy, N/A was used.

World Wide Web

A brief explanation of the job listings in Chapter Four: you will find the name of the site, followed by the URL. The **Number of job listings** is rounded down; for instance, if a site had 503 job listings, we said 500; if a site had 11,128 listings, we rounded that down to 11,100. **Types of jobs** indicates in general terms in what fields or job categories you are likely to find job listings. Similarly, **Locations of jobs** indicates for what countries, states, or cities job listings can be found. **Frequency of**

updates shows how often job listings are added to the database. **Search criteria available** shows you how the database can be searched. Most sites allow you to search by some combination of job category, location, company, or keywords; some let you search only by keyword. **Resume database available** indicates that the site accepts resumes. **Employer profiles available** means that the site lists employer profiles. **Costs for jobseekers to view/post a resume** and **Costs for employers to list job openings/view resumes** indicate applicable fees associated with using the service. Like the name indicates, **Other key features** discusses other career resources, besides job listings, available on the site. And **Insider tips** is our impression of a site and its resources, and other relevant information. **Note:** When we were unable to determine information within a reasonable degree of accuracy, N/A was used.

One Final Note

We recommend using the resources described in this book as a complement to your other job hunting methods. In other words, don't stop doing what has given you success in the past. Not everyone will want to, or should, use *all* the services mentioned. Instead, this book will help you determine which resources best meet *your* job hunting needs, so that you can start down the road to career success!

JOB HUNTING IN THE ELECTRONIC AGE

Looking for a new job can be a frustrating endeavor. Despite encouraging statistics that indicate healthy economic growth and the addition of new jobs, competition remains intense as millions of qualified and eager contenders flood the job market. A single help-wanted advertisement in the Sunday newspaper often yields hundreds of resumes from suitable applicants.

At the same time, new electronic technologies are changing our methods of communication—and job hunting is no exception. Employers are increasingly embracing these technologies as a means of recruiting and attracting the most suitable job candidates. For instance, a job opening posted on the Internet might receive a response within minutes, and also reaches a coverage area much greater than that of a newspaper advertisement. This means the applicant pool expands significantly.

Now this leads us to the questions plaguing all job hunters, regardless of their occupation or level of experience: How do I get ahead of the competition? Where can I find that winning edge that will land me a new job? Today, those answers often lie with technology. Like the employer who posts job openings on the Internet to find the right candidate, the same technologies can empower the job seeker to find the right job.

New advances in technology have given job hunters hundreds of new resources to turn to. Electronic resume and employment databases, job hunting software, and the Internet are just some of the advances that have made it easier than ever before to write high-quality resumes, make industry contacts, and uncover unadvertised job openings. And most experts agree that the ability to use these electronic resources effectively is becoming increasingly important in managing both an effective job hunt, and in the long run, your career.

The Electronic Revolution

Our society is in the middle of a revolution—a technological revolution that is radically changing the way we live. Just think back to twenty-five years ago—many of the conveniences we now take for granted, such as ATMs and VCRs, did not even exist!

This electronic revolution has had an enormous effect on the workplace. The use of personal computers, for instance, has tremendously boosted the productivity and efficiency of companies. Voice mail, fax machines, and more recently, email, have changed the way we communicate. Technology has created a global marketplace in which differences such as geography and language are no longer barriers for trade and communication.

A recent nationwide survey of corporations indicated that computer literacy and knowledge are the most important skills that managers look for when hiring new employees. This survey underscores the importance of technology in today's workplace. And for the job hunter, the message behind this survey is simple: If you fail to keep up, you may find yourself left behind.

Why Electronic Job Hunting?

Looking for a new job is rarely a pleasurable activity, but new advances in technology can help ease some of the stress normally associated with job hunting. With all the new resources available, relying only on the Sunday newspaper or old college friends to find job leads is no longer necessary. Electronic job hunting opens a whole new avenue of contacts and opportunities—areas that were previously hidden or otherwise unavailable to the general public. The following are some additional reasons to add electronic resources to your job hunting arsenal:

- As we mentioned earlier in this chapter, **an understanding and knowledge of computers is the most sought after skill in new employees.** Using electronic resources to find a job—even something as simple as emailing your resume to a company—is an easy way to demonstrate your computer skills to a potential employer. Any employer is sure to be impressed by anyone with the savvy and initiative to use this medium.

- **Submitting your resume to an electronic resume database or posting your resume online will put your skills on display** for the thousands of hiring managers and human resources professionals nationwide who regularly search these databases. This widespread exposure makes you a potential candidate for thousands of job openings that are *never* advertised. Plus, online discussion groups can help you form an international network of contacts in your field, which may be helpful when it comes time to look for a new job.

- **By using electronic business directories, either online or on CD-ROM, you can precisely identify those companies that hire employees in your field and with your background.** These databases also contain enough company information, such as press releases or financial statements, to give you a good indication of whether a particular company is right for you.

- **Not only are the Internet and commercial online services available to job hunters twenty-four hours a day, seven days a week,** but their national and international scopes are ideal for job hunters considering relocating to another city, state, or country.

- **Finally, you can find hundreds of thousands of job listings unavailable anywhere else** by using Gopher, Bulletin Board Systems, the Internet, and commercial online services. Not surprisingly, the huge collection of jobs available is the main reason most people turn to electronic job hunting.

Electronic vs. Online Job Hunting

Many people mistakenly believe that electronic job hunting is just another term for job hunting online. But that is not the case. Electronic job hunting means much more than simply logging on to the Internet and searching for job listings. Rather, **electronic job hunting means taking advantage of all the technological resources available** and using them to further your career.

Following are some more ideas to help you incorporate technology into your job search:

- **Write an electronic resume.** Having an electronic resume is virtually a necessity in today's job market. An electronic resume is simply a resume that is stripped of special formatting, making it easy for a computer to read. Once you prepare an electronic resume, you can submit it to an electronic resume database, or simply mail it out to your target employers. Many companies now have applicant tracking systems, which means that resumes are automatically entered into an in-house resume database that is searched whenever there's a job opening.

- **Research employers through commercial business databases.** Developing a target list of potential employers and researching a company in-depth for a job interview have become much simpler, thanks to electronic business databases like the JobBank List Service. Once available only as print directories, *JobBank* titles and other similar resources now offer much of the same information in CD-ROM or diskette versions, which makes them much easier (and faster) to search for specific information.

- **Use job hunting software.** Products such as Adams Job Interview Almanac and CD-ROM and WinWay Resume 6.0 offer a variety of electronic job hunting assistance. With the help of these and other programs, you can easily create a professional-quality resume and organize your contacts. You can also prepare for a job interview, often with a video interview tutorial, complete with sample questions and answers.

- **Prepare for computer-assisted job interviews and assessment tests.** With many companies, your first interview may well be with a computer, not a person. As impersonal as they sound, computer-assisted job interviews seem to be the wave of the future, especially in companies that hire large volumes of entry-level employees. Similarly, computerized assessment tests examine your skills, personality, and integrity in order to determine how well you will fit with a particular job.

Together, these two programs attempt to raise the quality of employees and lower turnover by ensuring that the employee fits the job.

Job Hunting Resources Available Online

Job hunters with online access have a vast selection of resources from which to choose. There are hundreds of services available that can help you with all aspects of the job hunt, including networking, researching companies, posting resumes, and—most importantly—finding job listings. Job hunting resources are found on both the Internet and commercial online services. Additionally, Bulletin Board Systems (BBSs), which represent a part of cyberspace that does not fall into either of these two areas, are also an excellent job hunting resource, particularly for job listings.

Commercial Online Services

These services, which charge users to access their resources, are more recognizable by their brand names: **America Online**, **CompuServe**, and **The Microsoft Network**. In general, they are excellent resources for networking and researching companies, although they also provide job listings. These services also provide their users with full access to the Internet and the vast employment resources available there. America Online (AOL) and CompuServe (owned by AOL) are the two largest commercial online services, and not surprisingly, they have the most resources to offer job hunters.

America Online is considered by many to have the strongest and largest collection of job listings available through a commercial online service. CompuServe, meanwhile, has dozens of high-quality professional discussion groups that are ideal for networking, as well as a number of searchable business databases that offer in-depth information on tens of thousands of companies, in both the United States and abroad. Microsoft has worked to get into the game through acquisitions and partnerships with various Internet software companies. The smaller services—like Delphi, and Prodigy—lack the quantity of resources presently found on AOL or CompuServe. At the same time, these services do provide their somewhat smaller base of users with a number of career resources, including discussion groups, job listings, and employer databases.

The Internet

The Internet, or ARPANET as it was originally called, was developed in 1969 by the United States government, which wanted to create a communications system for the exchange of scientific information. By the late 1980s the government began encouraging commercial use of the Internet. Thus, what was once the exclusive playground for academics and high-level government workers has grown into an international network of millions of users, with thousands more signing on every day.

There are four separate areas that are all part of the Internet: Gopher, Telnet, Usenet, and the World Wide Web. Together, Gopher, Usenet, and the Web represent the largest collection of job hunting information found online, including millions of job listings. It is no surprise, then, that when most people think of electronic job hunting, they think of the Internet.

- **Gopher.** Gopher is a menu-based system of organizing information on the Internet. It was also the first step in making the Internet more user-friendly, with its easy-to-manage menus and powerful search engines, Veronica and Jughead. Because it was developed at the University of Minnesota and quickly became a favorite of academics at other universities, Gopher remains a good source of academic and other specialized job listings. For example, it has one of the few employment resources found online that is dedicated to the arts. However, Gopher's popularity is fading in competition with the World Wide Web and Usenet newsgroups.

- **Usenet.** The User's Network is comprised of thousands of newsgroups, or electronic discussion groups, where people can exchange information, discuss ideas, or just chat. The very nature of Usenet makes it a natural for networking. With so many different newsgroups to choose from, you are sure to find one in your field of interest. Usenet also contains newsgroups dedicated to the posting of resumes and "situations wanted" messages, and is an *outstanding* resource for thousands of job listings.

- **The World Wide Web.** Currently, the Web is the best known area of the Internet, due mainly to the phenomenal growth it has experienced over the past several years. The Web has dozens of excellent electronic career centers that offer all kinds of job hunting advice and information, including an ever-growing number of large databases of job listings. In fact, the Web has by far the largest collection of job listings found online.

A Word of Caution

While enough cannot be said regarding the benefits of electronic job hunting, it's important to continue using traditional job hunting methods, such as attending professional seminars, tapping into your network of contacts, and contacting employers directly. The rule of never relying on only one method to find a job extends to electronic job hunting.

At the same time, resources such as job hunting software and electronic business databases can actually help you with a traditional job search. For example, a resume writing program can help you write a lively, professional-quality resume that is sure to get you noticed, and an employer database on CD-ROM can help you locate potential employers, who you can then contact through traditional methods.

Where to Begin

Now that you understand the benefits, as well as the limitations, of an electronic job hunt, you will need some basic equipment; namely, a computer, a modem, and an online or Internet service account. If you're a college or graduate student, you should have access through your college or university. Most schools now provide students with an Internet connection and an online account.

But if you're not a student and you don't already own a computer, you'll need to purchase the necessary hardware. Although more and more companies provide their employees with access to the Internet or a commercial online service, we strongly discourage you from using these resources at work, even after hours. It's not only a risky undertaking, but—because of the fee-based nature of the Internet and commercial services—borders on the unethical.

You have two choices of computers: a Macintosh or a PC-compatible machine. Macintoshes are much less common than PCs, and if you decide to buy one, you will have far fewer choices in terms of hardware, accessories, and software. A Macintosh with a System 8 operating system and a minimum of 32 MB memory is a solid choice. For a PC, buy at least a Pentium processor. Also, you'll want a Windows 95 or higher operating system, as well as at least 32 MB memory. A CD-ROM drive now comes standard on new computers, and this will be necessary if you want to use the job hunting software that's discussed in Chapter Seven. A 16x or 24x CD-ROM drive is your best bet.

As for modems, get the best and fastest modem that you can afford, which currently means a 56,600 BPS modem or better. Anything slower, such as a 28,800 BPS modem, could drive up your phone bills (if you're accessing through a long distance number), and using graphically rich services, such as the Web or America Online, will be painfully slow. With modems, quality matters as much, if not more, than speed. A high-quality modem has the ability to detect and correct errors in your phone line and connection.

Most new computers come with an internal modem already installed, but if you have an older computer that did not come with a modem, you'll need to purchase one. You can choose from either an internal or external modem.

You may want to consider an extra telephone line to connect to your modem. You can use your regular phone line, but you may, depending on your modem software, need to turn off any special features, such as call waiting, before you go online.

Next, you must decide whether you want to use a direct Internet connection or a commercial online service. (Remember, all commercial online services also provide full Internet access.) **Many newcomers choose a commercial online service, mainly because of the wide range of services offered and their ease of use.** You can subscribe to a service by installing the service's software, which is provided free of charge. You'll also commonly receive a free, one-month trial period. A commercial online service generally charges a flat monthly fee of about $20, which includes unlimited usage.

A direct Internet connection is generally the choice of experienced users, who are more inclined to know the subtleties and nuances of the Internet. You can buy Internet starter kits at a computer store, or look in the phone book for "Internet Service Providers" for instructions on how to sign up. In general, a direct Internet connection can cost as little as $10–$20 a month, often with an unlimited number of hours.

Online Strategies

Whether you choose a direct Internet connection or a commercial online service, take some time to become familiar with the service and the resources it offers. Check out some career areas, such as the big career centers on the Web. Lurk in a few discussion groups to get a sense of what they are really about. In addition to familiarizing yourself with a service, this process will also give you a good sense of how long it takes to find what you want online, so you'll be able to manage your time online better.

Try going online during off-peak hours, either early morning or late night. Services experience less traffic at these times, so it can be much easier to get through.

It's also a good idea to know what you want to accomplish *before* you go online. Have an agenda prepared, complete with keywords to search for, or the names and addresses of sites you want to visit. Again, this will save you time and money, depending on your account and connection. Also, having a plan will lessen the chances that you'll get sidetracked into a discussion group dealing with such issues as who should be cast in the next *Batman* movie.

On the Web, use search engines such as Yahoo!, Excite, and Alta Vista to help you find what you need in less time. These powerful search engines can help locate specific information and many will also search Usenet.

Don't rely on one particular area of the online world for all your job information. The World Wide Web is great, but don't forget those old reliables like Usenet newsgroups and Bulletin Board Systems, as well as offline options like career software. After you spend some time exploring, you'll probably discover that certain resources work best for you. Narrow your efforts to those areas, since the more focus you have, the more effective your job search will be.

Finally, be patient. It takes time to learn about all the resources described here, and you may not see any results from your efforts for some time. And even if you end up finding a new job in a traditional way, such as through a friend or in the newspaper, you have still learned valuable skills that will help you throughout your career.

PLUG IT IN: CREATE YOUR ELECTRONIC RESUME

With companies slashing recruiting budgets and trimming hiring staffs, employers rely increasingly on emerging technologies to find qualified candidates for job openings. Many companies use automated applicant tracking systems to process and sort employment applications. Other companies use the services of electronic employment database companies to fill specific openings. This means that your resume will be read by more computers and fewer people. Whether you're applying to a company that uses automated tracking systems or paying to have your resume loaded onto an electronic employment database, your resume must be in a format that is easy for a computer to recognize and understand. Otherwise, your application may quickly begin collecting dust.

Basically, this is how it works: Once a company receives your resume, it is fed through a scanner, which sends an image of the document to a computer. The computer "reads" your resume, looking for keywords, and then files your resume accordingly in its database. An employer who has bought access to an electronic employment database will search the database for applications that have keywords associated with the requirements of the position.

The good news about this technology is that it enables you to market your resume to thousands of employers quite easily. The bad news is that you must create an electronic resume in order to take advantage of the technology. But don't panic! An electronic resume is simply a modified version of your conventional resume. And though an electronic resume is very different from other types of resumes, it's easy to create.

But, before you go ahead and throw out your old paper resume, be advised that not all companies stay up to speed on the latest technology. Many companies simply don't have the equipment to directly receive emailed resumes and search online databases for job candidates. Thus, having a paper copy of your resume is still a necessity, especially since you'll need it to bring with you to all those job interviews!

Content

The information you include in your electronic resume does not greatly differ from a traditional resume, it's simply the manner in which you present this information that changes. Traditional books on resume writing tell you to include lots of action verbs, such as managed, coordinated, or developed, but now employers are more likely to do keyword searches using nouns, such as degree held or a software title you're familiar with. Personal traits are rarely used in keyword searches by employers, but when they are, traits like team player, creative, and problem-solving are among the most common. Following is a list of the basic information you should include in your resume:

- **Name.** Your name should appear at the top of your resume, with your address immediately below.
- **Abbreviations.** Most resume scanning systems will recognize a few common abbreviations like BS, MBA, and state names. Widely used acronyms for industry jargon, such as A/R and A/P on an accounting resume, are also generally accepted. But if there's any question about whether an abbreviation is a standard one, play it safe and spell it out.
- **Keywords.** As noted above, using the right keywords or key phrases are critical elements in developing your electronic resume. For example, let's say an employer searches an employment database for a sales representative with the following keyword criteria:

sales representative
BS/BA

> exceeded quota
> cold calls
> high energy
> willing to travel

Even if you have the right qualifications, if you don't use these keywords on your resume, the computer will pass over your application. To complicate matters further, different employers search for different keywords. These are usually buzzwords common to your field or industry that describe your experience, education, skills, and abilities. You should be careful to place the most important words first on the list, since the computer may be limited in the number of words it will read. Common keywords may be found by checking help-wanted advertisements for job openings in your field. What terms do employers commonly use to describe their requirements? Executive recruiters who specialize in your field are also a good source of this kind of information. Of course, you'll want to use as many different keywords in your resume as possible to maximize your chances.

- **Keyword Summary.** This is an inventory of your qualifications, usually written in a series of succinct keyword phrases that immediately follow your name and address.
- **Career Objective.** As with traditional resumes, including a career objective is optional. If you choose to use a job objective, try to keep it general so as not to limit your opportunities. After all, while the computer does the initial screening, your resume will eventually be seen by a human hiring manager. Your objective should express a general interest in a particular field or industry ("an entry-level position in advertising"), but should not designate a specific job title ("a position as Senior Agency Recruitment Specialist"). You should try to include a few keywords in the objective as well, in order to increase your chances of getting matched ("a position as a financial analyst where I can utilize my on-the-job experience and MBA").
- **Experience and Achievements.** Your professional experience should immediately follow the keyword summary, beginning with your most recent position. (If you are a recent college

graduate, however, you should list your education before your experience.) Be sure that your job title, employer, location, and dates of employment are all clearly displayed. Highlight your accomplishments and key responsibilities with bullets. Again, try to incorporate as many keywords as possible into these phrases.

- **Education.** This section immediately follows the experience section. List your degrees, licenses, permits, certifications, relevant course work, and academic awards or honors. Be sure to clearly display the names of the schools, locations, and years of graduation. You should also list any professional organizations or associations that you belong to; many recruiters will include such organizations when doing a keyword search.

- **References.** Don't waste valuable space with statements like "References available upon request." Although this section was standard fare for resumes of old, it won't win you any points on an electronic resume. Similarly, don't include personal data, such as your birthdate or marital status, or information regarding your hobbies and interests. Since it is unlikely that these sections would include any keywords, they are only taking up space, and the computer will pass right over them.

Should You Include a Cover Letter with Your Electronic Resume?

Yes. While your cover letter will not help you in the initial selection process, it can help distinguish you from the competition in the final rounds of elimination. If you've taken the time to craft a letter that summarizes your strongest qualifications, you'll have the edge over other contenders who skip this important step.

As with your resume, your cover letter should contain keywords reflecting your strongest qualifications. If you're responding to a classified ad, try to use many of the same keywords that the ad mentions. And if you're sending your resume to a new networking contact, be sure to mention who referred you. Even in this anonymous electronic age, the old adage "it's all in who you know" still holds true.

ELECTRONIC COVER LETTER

69 Pageant Drive
Cambridge, MA 02138
(617) 555-5555

September 3, 1999

Ms. Natalie Goldword
Controller
Any Corporation
1140 Bones Street
Boston, MA 02215

Dear Ms. Goldword:

This letter is in response to your September 2 advertisement in the *Boston Globe* for the position of Assistant Controller. I am very interested in the position and believe I have the qualifications you are looking for. Please consider the following:

- Over twenty years experience in Accounting and Systems Management, Budgeting, Forecasting, Cost Containment, Financial Reporting, and International Accounting.
- Implemented a "team-oriented" cross-training program within accounting group, resulting in timely month-end closings and increased productivity of key accounting staff.
- MBA in Management from Northeastern University.
- Results-oriented professional and proven team leader.

These are only a few of my credentials that may be of interest to you. I look forward to discussing them with you further in a personal interview. Thank you for your consideration.

Sincerely,
Michael S. Dipe

Formatting the Electronic Resume

Keep your electronic resume simple. Remember, a computer will often look at your resume before a person does. The same elaborate formatting that makes your resume beautiful to the human eye makes it impossible for a computer to understand. Following are some basic rules concerning how to format your resume:

- **Length of the Resume.** Ideally your resume should be one to two pages in length. If you go over one page, make sure your name appears at the top of each subsequent page. Always use a second sheet of paper if your resume is longer than one page—never try to print the second page on the back of the first.

- **Paper.** Don't bother with expensive paper or fancy colors. Use standard, twenty pound, 8½" x 11" paper. Because your resume needs to be as sharp and legible as possible, your best bet is to use black ink on white paper.

- **Font.** Stick to the basics; this is no time to express your creativity. Choose a nondecorative font with clear, distinct characters, such as Helvetica or Times. It is more difficult for a scanner to accurately pick up more decorative fonts, such as script or serif fonts.

- **Font Size.** A font size of 12 points is ideal. Don't go below 10 or above 14 points, as type that is too small or too large is difficult for a scanner to read.

- **Font Style.** Most scanners will accept boldface, but if a potential employer specifically instructs you to avoid it, you can substitute boldface with all capital letters. Boldface and all capitals are best used only for major section headings, such as "Experience" and "Education." Avoid using boldface type for your name, address, and telephone number. It's also best to avoid using italics or underlining, since this can cause the letters to bleed into each other, or worse, make the words unintelligible. You can also use dashes (--) or asterisks (*) to emphasize certain accomplishments or experiences.

- **Graphics, Lines, and Shading.** Avoid the temptation to use lines and graphics to liven up what is an otherwise visually uninteresting resume. A resume scanner will try to "read" graphics, lines, and shading as text, resulting in computer chaos. You should also avoid using nontraditional layouts for your resume, such as two-column formats.

- **White Space.** Don't try to compress space between letters, words, or lines in order to fit everything on one page. When you do this, there's a greater chance that the words and letters will bleed into each other, making it more difficult for the computer to read your resume. Many job seekers feel compelled to squeeze as much information as possible onto a single sheet of paper, but you should always leave plenty of space between sections on your resumes. It's easier for a scanner to "read" your resume with accuracy if there are distinct breaks between sections.

- **Printing.** Whatever type of printing process you use, make sure the end result is letter quality. Ideally, you should have it printed at your local copy shop. Otherwise, a laser printer is perfectly acceptable. Avoid typewriters and dot matrix printers, since the quality of type they produce is inadequate for most scanners. Because your resume needs to be as sharp and legible as possible, you should always send originals, not photocopies. For the same reason, you should always mail, not fax, your resume, unless specifically instructed to do so. And if your resume is longer than one page, don't staple the pages together.

ELECTRONIC RESUME

MICHAEL S. DIPE
69 Pageant Drive
Cambridge, MA 02138
(617) 555-5555

KEYWORD SUMMARY

Senior financial manager with over twenty years experience in Accounting and Systems Management, Budgeting, Forecasting, Cost Containment, Financial Reporting, and International Accounting. MBA in Management. Proficient in Lotus, Excel, Solomon, Real World, and Windows.

PROFESSIONAL EXPERIENCE

COLWELL CORPORATION, Wellesley, MA
$100 Million Division of Bancroft Corporation

Director of Accounting and Budgets, 1988–present
Direct staff of twenty in General Ledger, Accounts Payable, Accounts Receivable, and International Accounting. Facilitate month-end closing process with parent company and auditors.

- Implement "team-oriented" cross-training program within accounting group, resulting in timely month-end closings and increased productivity of key accounting staff.
- Developed and implemented a strategy for Sales and Use Tax Compliance in all fifty states with 100 percent compliance for both parent company and subsidiaries.
- Prepare monthly financial statements and analyses for review by management executive board.

Accounting Manager, 1985–1988
Managed a staff of six in General Ledger and Accounts Payable. Responsible for the design and refinement of financial reporting package. Assisted in month-end closing.

- Established guidelines for month-end closing procedures, thereby speeding up closing by five business days.
- Promoted to Director of Accounting and Budgets.

MICHAEL S. DIPE
(page 2)

FRANKLIN AND DELANY COMPANY, Melrose, MA

Senior Accountant, 1979–1985
Managed A/P, G/L, transaction processing, and financial reporting.
Supervised staff of two.
* Developed Management Reporting package, including variance reports
  and cash flow reporting.

Staff Accountant, 1975–1979
Managed A/P, including vouchering, cash disbursements, and bank
reconciliation. Wrote and issued policies. Maintained supporting schedules
used during year-end audits. Trained new employees.

Junior Accountant, 1973–1975
Assisted in general ledger closing. Monitored cash collections and
accounts receivable.

EDUCATION

MBA in Management, Northeastern University, Boston, MA, 1985
BS in Accounting, Boston College, Boston, MA, 1973

ASSOCIATIONS

National Association of Accountants

Preparing a Resume for the Web

In addition to being read by scanners, resumes also need to be Web-friendly. In other words, your resume also needs to be in a format that you can send to employers and online databases electronically through cyberspace. Why is this important? Companies are increasingly requesting that resumes be submitted through email, and many recruiters regularly check online resume databases for candidates to fill unadvertised job openings.

There are three basic ways to get your resume on the Internet. If you have a plain text resume, you can post your resume to an online resume database or email it directly to a potential employer. Or, you can create a resume in HTML and post it to special sites on the Web that accept HTML resumes. You can even design your own home page for potential employers to visit. HTML (hypertext markup language) is the text formatting language used to publish information on the World Wide Web.

Online resume databases are very similar to electronic employment databases. Simply put, they are large databases of resumes that employers search when looking for job candidates. Submitting your resume to an online resume database is a relatively inexpensive method (sometimes free) of exposing your resume to a large audience, including thousands of human resources professionals at major corporations and independent recruiters. Online resume databases are generally found on Usenet newsgroups or the World Wide Web. Many databases can also be accessed through commercial online services. Monster.com and CareerMosaic, for example, both have resume databases that can be accessed through America Online (**keyword: Career Center**).

Emailing your resume directly to potential employers is generally done in response to a help-wanted advertisement or simply as a method of direct contact. In fact, many companies now request that resumes be submitted through email, rather than the U.S. mail or by fax. Many job listings you find on the Internet, particularly for technical positions, include only an email address for contact information; no street address or telephone number is provided. And with many companies, you can email your resume directly into their in-house resume database. This eliminates the concern that your resume will be found unreadable by a computerized resume scanner.

The usefulness of HTML resumes is still being explored. Many of the major online databases do not accept HTML resumes, and the vast majority of companies only accept plain text resumes through their email. At the same time, new sites that do accept HTML resumes are constantly cropping up on the Web, as are job seekers showing off their skills on their own home pages. Generally, this is more common and useful for those job seekers who are involved in Web design. Therefore, we are focusing on plain text resumes, online databases, and the protocol of emailing resumes to potential employers, while HTML resumes and creating your own home page are only discussed briefly. Multimedia and video resumes are also discussed briefly at the end of this chapter.

Converting Your Resume to a Plain Text File

Remember, an electronic resume is one that is sparsely formatted, but filled with keywords and important facts. If you have already prepared a resume that is computer-friendly, you don't have that far to go to be able to post your resume on the Internet. A plain text resume is the next step in creating a truly electronic resume. But before you panic and start thinking that you need to create yet another resume, rest assured that you can easily convert your regular resume to one that can be transmitted electronically.

In order to post your resume to the Internet, you will need to change the way your resume is formatted. Instead of a Microsoft Word, WordPerfect, or other word processing document, save your resume as a plain text, DOS, or ASCII file. These three terms are basically inter-changeable; different software will use different terms. These words all describe text at its most basic level, without the formatting such as boldface and italics that we all like to use to make our documents look more interesting. Furthermore, an ASCII document appears on the recipient's screen as left-aligned. If you have email, you'll notice that most of your messages are written and received in this format. ASCII, which stands for American Standard Code for Information Interchange, is simply a code that virtually all computers can understand. It was invented to allow different types of computers to easily exchange infor-mation. By converting your resume to a plain text, or ASCII file, you can be assured your resume and other files will be readable regardless of where you send them. Otherwise, your resume may be unreadable.

Before you attempt to create your own plain text resume, study the resumes on the online databases. This will give you a good idea of what a plain text resume looks like, and will help you to create your own resume. Following are the basic steps for creating a plain text resume (the particulars of the process will differ, depending on what type of computer system and software you're using):

- **Remove all formatting from your resume**. See "Formatting the Electronic Resume" on page 26.
- **Convert your resume to a plain text file**. Most word pro-cessing programs, such as WordPerfect and Microsoft Word,

have a "save as" feature that allows you to save files to different formats. For instance, in Microsoft Word for Windows, saving a document as a Word document, as a text-only document, or as a WordPerfect document are just some of your options. Many programs—like Microsoft Word—don't specifically give you an "ASCII" option; in these programs, you should choose "text only" or "plain text." In Microsoft Word, plain text files have the extension *.txt.

- **After saving your resume as a plain text file, check the document with the text editor** that most computers have. In Windows 95, use the Notepad from the accessories group found in Program Manager.

- **Open the file to be sure that your margins look right and that you don't have extra spaces between lines or letters**. If parts of the text look garbled with a group of strange characters, it most likely means that you forgot to take out some formatting. A resume with a lot of formatting is likely to end up looking like hieroglyphics if it's read as a plain text file. If this happens, you need to go back to your original document and repeat the process.

- **Be sure that all your lines contain sixty-five characters or less**. This includes all spacing, letters, and punctuation. Often, you will need to go through your entire resume line-by-line, counting each space, letter, punctuation, asterisks, and so forth. You may need to manually insert hard returns where the lines are longer than sixty-five characters. This may seem trivial, but it is extremely important. While some computers may recognize as many as seventy-five characters, the majority cannot recognize more than sixty-five characters per line. So just to be on the safe side, don't go longer than sixty-five characters.

- Finally, **email your resume to yourself or to a friend in order to test the file**. Be sure that your resume stayed intact, that no extra spaces or returns were inserted during the transmission, and that all text appears readable. If something doesn't look right, go back to your text editor, fix the problem, and test the resume again before emailing it to any companies or posting it to online databases.

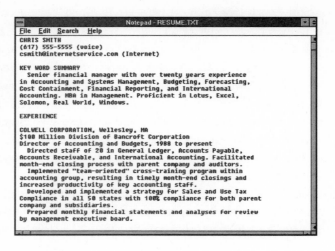

Emailing Your Resume Directly to a Company

Another way to get your resume noticed is to email it directly to an employer. As mentioned previously, more and more companies are requesting that resumes be submitted through email. This is especially true for companies that post their job listings on the Internet. In fact, many online job listings will not even contain an address or a phone number. And if you look at your Sunday help-wanted advertisements, you are likely to find that the ads will often give an email address, along with a mailing address or fax number, where candidates can submit resumes.

Email has several advantages over traditional postal mail. Emailing your resume is quick and efficient, for both you and your target company. Rather than spending time printing out a copy of your resume, addressing an envelope, and mailing it, you can simply send your resume with a few clicks of your mouse. This allows you to respond almost instantly to job listings online, as well as ads you see in the newspaper. This means that you can be among the first candidates a hiring manager evaluates. Also, many employers like emailed resumes because they cut down on paperwork and lower administrative costs.

With that said, it's important to be aware of the proper procedure for emailing your resume to a specific company. While it's generally preferable to send a resume to a specific individual, rather than to a company's human resources department, you are more likely to find the email address for the human resources department than for a specific department manager or supervisor. The generic employment mailbox is usually the address given in help-wanted ads or on the company's home page, and unsolicited resumes sent to a general human resources mailbox are likely to end up in an in-house resume database. However, if the resume was emailed in response to a specific advertisement, the chances are greater that the resume will actually be viewed by an individual.

If you do find the email address of a specific manager or supervisor, don't simply send them your resume "cold." Be sure to call or email that manager first to be sure that he or she is the right person to receive your resume, and to find out how you should send the resume—in the body of the email message or as an attachment.

Once you know the correct email address and other information, you can prepare your email message. Remember, you should only email your resume *after* you have first tested it by sending it to yourself or to a friend. Here are the steps to take to email your resume:

- **Log on to your email account** and choose the option for a new message.
- **Type in the email address and subject**. For the subject, say something like, "Resume, entry-level accountant."
- **Paste your resume into the body of your email message, or type in the resume file name as an attachment file**.
- **Proofread** the message.
- **Send** the email.

After you email your resume, wait a few days so you can be sure that someone has read it. Call or email the company to confirm that your resume was received intact. As with a paper resume, an emailed resume may do you little good unless you follow up to express your genuine interest in the company or the position. If you sent your resume to an individual, ask if he or she would like you to elaborate on any sections of your resume. Similarly, if you sent your resume to a general email address, call the human resources department to check the status of your application. Assuming they have an in-house resume database and applicant tracking system, they should be able to tell you whether or not the email was received.

As for cover letters, experts disagree on whether you should email one along with your resume. Some human resources professionals maintain that the cover letter, especially if it's contained in a separate file, is a nuisance. Others say a cover letter is still a job hunting necessity. Of course, if a company specifically requests one in a job listing, don't simply ignore the request. If, however, an ad makes no mention of a cover letter, your best bet is to call the human resources department and ask about sending one.

Circulating Your Electronic Resume

Once you have designed a computer-friendly resume, there are three possible ways to circulate it (in addition to directly emailing your resume to an employer). The first involves an electronic employment database service. For what is usually a minimal fee, you can send your electronic gem to one of these services, where it will be filed in a database containing up to tens of thousands of resumes. When outside companies need candidates for a job opening, they contact the service, and provide a list of qualifications (or keywords) the position requires. The service will then search the database (using a keyword search) to find suitable candidates.

The second way to circulate your resume is to send it to a company with an in-house resume database, or applicant tracking system. With these systems, your resume is scanned into the company's database. Whenever there's an opening, the hiring manager submits a search request, which generally includes a job description and a list of keywords to search for. Again, operators will search the database to come up with viable candidates.

The last way to make use of your electronic resume is to post it directly onto the Internet, either to an online database service, a commercial online service, a newsgroup, or a site on the World Wide Web. Basically, online databases work the same way as electronic employment databases. Once you post your resume to a specified site on the Internet, it becomes available to the increasing number of corporate recruiters who regularly search the Internet for job candidates.

Electronic Employment Databases

How would you feel if you were told you could contact hundreds, or even thousands, of potential employers with a single copy of your resume—ecstatic, relieved, hopeful? Well, with the help of an electronic employment database, that is exactly what you can do.

An electronic employment database is simply a resume database operated by independent commercial firms. These databases can contain tens of thousands of resumes from all levels of job seekers—college graduates to experienced corporate executives. The procedure for submitting resumes to these services varies, and some do charge a minimal fee. But what you get for your money is often well worth it: nationwide exposure to hundreds of companies of all sizes, from *Fortune* 500 to smaller, rapidly expanding companies.

In many ways, an electronic resume database is very similar to a traditional employment agency: you submit your resume to a service, and the service begins working to find a job for you. However, with an electronic employment "agency," you are—theoretically—in the running for every job request that comes into a company, thanks to the use of keyword searches. While each resume database service is different, it generally works as follows:

- **You submit your resume to an electronic employment database service.** Some companies charge a small fee, usually around $30 to $50. Some services will also send you a "professional profile" sheet to fill out. Essentially an employment application, these forms ask you to indicate your work experiences, skills, and other information, such as geographical preferences or willingness to relocate. This form is used either in addition to, or instead of, your resume.
- **Your resume and/or professional profile is scanned** or entered into the computer system.
- **Client companies call the service with job openings**, and give the database service a list of keywords and desired qualifications. Some services allow employers online access to the database so they can do the search themselves.
- **The database is searched for suitable candidates** who match the keywords provided by the client.

- **The service provides the client with a list of possible candidates.** Again, how the candidates are presented varies according to the service. Some services provide candidate summaries, others provide the actual resume, while still others also include the additional information that the candidate provided on his or her "professional profile."

- **The client company sorts through the list of possible candidates, and then contacts desirable candidates directly.** Some services, however, will call you before forwarding your resume or any information to the client company.

Electronic employment databases offer tremendous advantages to both the job seeker and the recruiting company. A job seeker can easily be exposed to hundreds of companies with only one resume at little to no cost. In the past, it would take job hunters hours of research to come up with the company names, addresses, and contact names of potential employers. Plus, job hunters had the additional cost of stationery, printing, and postage to mail out those hundreds of resumes. Also, job hunters are exposed to employers nationwide, not just in their own town or region. So if you are willing to relocate, you can find your dream job even if it's thousands of miles away!

For employers, resume database services can potentially save companies hours of work. Instead of putting a costly job advertisement in the newspaper or a trade publication, and then spend time looking through hundreds of responses, companies can simply contact a resume database service, and the service will do the work for them. In effect, these services prescreen candidates. The use of the keyword search ensures that employers won't waste time reviewing resumes of candidates who lack the proper qualifications for a position. While no company relies entirely on this method, many companies use it as a first step in the search for qualified candidates, often because the database will give them a better idea of the available talent pool. For instance, if a database search turned up only a few qualified candidates, the recruiter may re-evaluate the minimum qualifications and skills for a given position.

Many job seekers are wary of resume database services because of issues of confidentiality. What if you submit your resume to a database service, only to have it land on your boss' desk? Many services offer safeguards to ensure this doesn't happen. Some database services allow you to submit names of companies you would prefer did not receive your resume. Others will contact you to get your permission before forwarding your resume or employment profile to a company. Still others allow you to join the database anonymously—that is, your name, company names, education, and any other identifiable characteristics will not be shown to prospective employers. Again, check with different services to determine their particular policies, and find out if the employer will see your actual resume or just a candidate profile or summary.

Of course, each electronic employment database is different. For instance, some services only accept resumes from alumni of particular universities, while others market to a specific demographic. Also, the fees that services charge can vary; however, through researching this book, we found fewer services charging a fee than had in the previous edition.

The following is a listing of selected electronic employment databases. **Note:** Be sure to check with each service before sending your resume or any registration fees. With today's rapidly-changing technology, procedures or fees can change quickly.

cors
One Pierce Place, Suite 300 East, Itasca IL 60143
800-323-1352
Fax: 630-250-7362
This service boasts of having almost 1.5 million resumes in their database. With over 6,000 clients, the service matches about 200 jobs each month. The firm attracts clients in all fields— computers, health care, finance, engineering, and communications. You can join this service for a one-time fee of $25; simply mail your resume to the address indicated. Once the service receives your resume, you will receive a confirmation letter in the mail that includes an identification number, which you can use to check on the status of your resume or to make free updates to it.

DORS
DMDC/Operation Transition
P. O. Box 130, Seaside CA 93955
800-727-3677
Fax: 831-583-2475

This is a resume database service for military personnel and workers in select civil service organizations who are leaving the military or civil service to work in the private sector. The goal of the service is to help military personnel make a successful transition to civilian life by giving candidates exposure to a wide range of companies in diverse fields and locations. Military personnel receive information on this service as part of their transition training. This service is also available for the spouses of military personnel. According to information supplied by DORS, more than 20,000 employers have registered to use the service. This service is offered to both jobseekers and employers at no cost.

Electronic Job Matching
HRMC (Human Resource Management Center)
4012 Gunn Highway, Suite 120, Tampa FL 33624
813-879-4200
Fax: 813-870-1883
Email address: ejm@hrmc.com

The Electronic Job Matching Database is free to all jobseekers, and currently contains over 30,000 resumes. More than 700 employers actively search the database, including private-sector companies in all fields and industries, from communications and law to manufacturing and health care. To enter the database, simply mail your resume to the address indicated. Your resume will be scanned into the system, and the computer will create a personalized "electronic portfolio." Jobseekers can specify certain search criteria, such as location, salary, or industry. Resumes that are emailed to HRMC can use a variety of formats, while resumes that are either faxed or sent through postal mail to HRMC should use a simple, plain format.

University ProNet
2445 Faber Place, Palo Alto CA 94303-3316
Web address: http://www.universitypronet.com

University ProNet is a resume database serving more than 100,000 alumni, and is sponsored by twenty-one of the country's leading universities: California Institute of Technology; Carnegie-Mellon University; Columbia University; Cornell University; Duke; Georgia Tech; Massachusetts Institute of Technology; Purdue; Ohio State University; Stanford University; U.S. Naval Academy; University of California at Berkeley; UCLA; University of Chicago; University of Illinois; University of Michigan; University of North Carolina; University of Pennsylvania; University of Texas at Austin; University of Wisconsin; and Yale University. The service is open only to the alumni of these universities, but it is accessible to over 400 companies. One-time fees run about $50; the fee varies slightly depending on the school. If you hold a degree from one of these universities, contact your alumni association for more information on how to join this service. You can also visit University ProNet's Website at **http://www.universitypronet.com**.

Applicant Tracking Systems

As the name implies, applicant tracking systems, or in-house resume databases, are used by companies to keep track of the hordes of resumes they receive. Many companies, especially large, well-known companies, can receive an average of two hundred resumes per week. Where once these unsolicited resumes may have headed straight for a filing cabinet, or even the trash—never to be looked at again—electronic applicant tracking systems now allow employers to keep resumes in an active file, in some cases indefinitely.

An in-house resume database functions much the same way as a commercial employment database. Basically, here's how it works:

- **A company receives your resume**, either unsolicited, through a career fair, or in response to a classified advertisement.
- **Your resume is scanned into the computer**, where it becomes part of a large pool of talent, often consisting of thousands of resumes.
- **Your resume is dated, coded, and placed into the appropriate file**, such as administrative, financial, or technical. Other systems may simply sort resumes according to date received.

- **Whenever there's a job opening, hiring managers simply submit search requests to the database operator**, who is usually someone in either human resources or information systems.

- **The database operator performs keyword searches** in order to find resumes that match the criteria that the hiring manager has provided.

- **The database operator provides the hiring manager with the resumes** (or candidate summaries) of those candidates who meet the criteria, at which point the hiring process continues in the traditional manner.

As previously discussed, companies prefer this new technology because it's more efficient, in terms of both time and money. The automated system cuts down on paperwork for many human resources managers, and subsequently lowers administrative costs. Also, in major cities like New York or Los Angeles, classified advertising can cost thousands of dollars. With efficient applicant tracking systems, companies can simply dip into their established pool of candidates.

There's also less of a chance that your resume will get lost on someone's desk or in a filing cabinet. When resumes are received, they're immediately scanned and put on file electronically. Providing, of course, that your resume was computer-friendly and scannable, you don't have to worry about your resume getting misplaced accidentally.

Finally, an applicant tracking system will increase the chances of your finding a position within a specific company. Consider this scenario: You send in your resume in response to a help-wanted advertisement. Your resume is filed into the company's in-house resume database. You're passed over for that position, but three months later, a similar position opens up. When the database is searched, your resume comes up as a possible match. Your resume is passed along to the hiring manager, who decides to bring you in for an interview, and four weeks later, you're offered the position.

In the days before this technology, you had little chance of landing another job within a company if you were passed over initially. Most likely, your resume would have been thrown out after you were passed over the first time, and you would never even have had an opportunity to apply for the second position. **However, with an electronic applicant tracking system, your resume is automatically kept in the database, where—because of the use of keyword searches—you remain in contention for every job opening.**

An electronic applicant tracking system also eliminates the need to send in multiple resumes to the same company. Before, a job seeker may have sent in resumes to three or four different department managers. Now, just one submission is necessary, since your resume is kept in a company-wide database where it is accessible to every hiring manager. If, however, you do send in multiple resumes, the system will usually throw out the old one and keep the most recent resume on file.

Still, there are two major disadvantages to automated applicant tracking systems. The first is the impersonal nature of the system. A computer will look for only those resumes that exactly meet the strict criteria of the search. This tends to put recent college graduates or those switching careers at a disadvantage, since these job seekers are less likely to have as many keywords included in their resumes. Borderline candidates may be passed over by a computer search because they only have six out of ten desired keywords. These same candidates may have been brought in for interviews if a recruiter noticed some special accomplishment or trait which the computer wasn't asked to look for.

Another problem is the technology itself. No automated system is infallible—there's always a chance that the computer will reject your resume, thereby taking you out of contention for any job openings. If, for example, the scanner is unable to read your resume, or turns it into an unintelligible mess, you are out of luck. If this is the case, don't expect the database operator to call you and ask you to send in a new resume. Therefore, it is imperative that you follow the steps discussed earlier in order to design a clean, computer-friendly resume.

Why Use Online Resume Databases?

Why post your resume to an online database? In a word: exposure! Recent reports indicate that more than twenty million people worldwide have access to the Internet, including thousands of human resources professionals and recruiters. Why *wouldn't* you want your skills to have that breadth of exposure?

By posting your resume online, you are essentially marketing yourself to the thousands of human resources professionals and hiring managers worldwide who are using the Internet in ever increasing numbers, either to post job listings or to search resume databases for job candidates. **Online databases allow recruiters and hiring managers to search through large pools of candidates quickly and easily**, using keywords to identify only those candidates who have the right qualifications for a given position. Many recruiters report that job candidates found online tend to be of a higher quality than those found through, perhaps, a newspaper advertisement. Candidates who use the Internet have the advanced computer skills that are becoming increasingly important in today's job market, and many recruiters like to see those who take the initiative to embrace this new technology.

Another reason to use an online resume database is its reach. If you are considering relocating, posting your resume in an online database is a good way to get it circulating in another city before you even move. Most job hunting sites on the World Wide Web are searched by recruiters nationwide—even worldwide—and there are also a number of regional databases (mostly newsgroups) where you can post your resume. So if you live in Baltimore and you want to find a job in San Francisco, you could post your resume to **ba.jobs.resumes**, a Usenet newsgroup for resume posting in the San Francisco Bay area.

At the same time, many job hunters are wary of putting their lives on display for anyone to see. When your resume is online, it's accessible to virtually anyone with a computer and an Internet connection. This includes personal information, such as your name, address, and telephone number. It is this lack of control over who sees their resume that worries most job seekers. Since you have no control over who sees your resume, you may receive phone calls or email messages from companies, organizations, and individuals you have absolutely no interest in working for.

Although many databases will hide your personal information from employers until after they've bought your resume, many other resume databases do not offer anonymity to their users. And while some services restrict access to their resume database only to subscribers, that is only seldom the case. Before you post your resume online, consider where you want to post it and who may see it (manager, co-worker, etc.).

Where to Post Your Resume Online

Cyberspace offers three main areas for resume posting: Usenet newsgroups, commercial online services, and the World Wide Web. These sites range from the general newsgroup (**misc.jobs.misc**) to the specific Website (**http://www.jobs4hr.com**). Of the three areas, you'll find the most options on the World Wide Web. Virtually all of the major job hunting sites on the Web, such as the Monster.com and CareerPath, offer resume databases where job hunters can post their resumes. The Web also contains dozens of other sites for resume posting, including the only sites where you can post HTML resumes.

Given all the choices available, you may be wondering how to decide where to post your resume. Since most online resume databases don't charge job seekers, you could—theoretically—post your resume to every site. However, since that's not necessarily practical, the best approach is to visit a database of potential interest to see what types of resumes are in that database. For instance, if you visit a site where most resumes showcase technical backgrounds, then it's a safe bet that most of the companies that search that database are looking to fill technical positions. If you have a background in finance, you would likely be wasting your time by posting your resume there. Similarly, if you notice that most resumes show little experience, you may have stumbled upon a posting site for new graduates. If you have ten solid years of work experience, it would likely do little good to post your resume there. Finally, if you are thinking of posting your resume to a general job posting site, such as Monster.com, check out what companies advertise in their job listings sections. Generally, those same sponsors will be the primary companies to scan the database for candidates.

Most online sites do not charge for posting your resume; charges, if any, are usually incurred by client employers and recruiters. However, some—especially those run by independent recruiters or career placement services—do charge a small fee. Sometimes those fees include resume preparation and advice. At the same time, those type of resume databases are smaller and do not have the broad exposure that some of the larger, free databases have. But if you feel you need help composing your resume, the fee might just be worth it. **Note**: Before you write a check or give your credit card number to a company over the Internet, it's a good idea to check its reputation with the Better Business Bureau or a similar agency. While the majority of companies selling services over the Internet are reputable, remember that simply because a company has a presence on the Internet does not mean it is honest and legitimate.

Commercial Online Services

Commercial online services, like America Online, CompuServe, and The Microsoft Network are, in comparison to newsgroups and the Web, fairly limited in what they offer in terms of resume posting services. However, these services have easy access to both newsgroups and the Web, so you can easily use the resume posting resources available there. Please refer to Chapter Two for more information on commercial online services.

Newsgroups

Usenet newsgroups tend to be more focused in scope, in terms of both region and subject matter. By posting your resume in a newsgroup, it is more likely to be seen by a local employer, or one that really matches your interests, than if you put your resume in a large national database. What's the point of having twenty employers call to request interviews if they are all in San Diego and you live in Baltimore?

Note: Usenet newsgroups tend to follow strict protocol. Most newsgroups contain postings with advice that outlines the protocol for that particular newsgroup. Be sure to read these *before* posting your resume. Finally, be careful not to post your resume to just any newsgroup with the word "job" in the address, since not every job-related newsgroup accepts resume postings. See Chapter Three for more information and a listing of career-related newsgroups.

The World Wide Web

Resume sites on the Web typically contain resumes from jobseekers across the country, which means that employers nationwide search the databases for potential candidates. For this reason, it's a good idea to add a line to your resume stating whether you are willing to relocate. And like newsgroups, you will need to come up with a title—or subject line—for your resume. Most experts suggest simply using your desired job title as the title for your resume.

The following are just eight of the major job hunting sites on the Web. These sites, as with many career Websites, offer both job search and resume services:

CareerCity
http://www.careercity.com
CareerMart
http://www.careermart.com
CareerMosaic
http://www.careermosaic.com
CareerShop
http://www.careershop.com
CareerSite
http://www.careersite.com
E-Span's JobOptions
http://www.joboptions.com/esp/plsql/
espan_enter.espan_home
JobBank USA
http://www.jobbankusa.com
Monster.com
http://www.monster.com

Targeted Sites on the World Wide Web

Many sites on the Web where you can post your resume are regional or geared towards a specific field or experience level. Some accept only HTML resumes or ASCII resumes, while others accept both. Keep in mind that some of the lesser known sites described in the following list may charge a fee for entering your resume into the database.

This list is only a sample of additional sites you will find on the Web. There are more of these sites popping up all the time, but the following list should get your search off to a solid start.

Again, the biggest advantage of these systems is that employers and recruiters like them because they are efficient. With these databases, employers have almost instant access to hundreds, if not thousands, of resumes. And this efficiency translates into lower administrative costs, which is a goal of all companies.

Canadian Resume Centre
> http://www.canres.com

Colorado Online Job Connection
> http://www.coloradojobs.com

The Internet Job Locator
> http://www.joblocator.com/jobs/

monster Healthcare
> http://www.medsearch.com

Shawn's Internet Resume Center
> http://www.inpursuit.com/sirc/seeker.html

The World Wide Web Resume Bank
> http://www.careermag.com

Bulletin Board Systems and Gopher

These services are not generally considered destinations for resume posting, and are best used to find job listings or to gather information regarding specific industries and potential employers. While you may post resumes to most Bulletin Board Systems, they are not a very efficient way to circulate your resume. For this reason, you're better off sticking to sites on the Web and Usenet newsgroups.

How to Post Your Resume Online

Most sites have their own specific instructions for entering a resume into their database. These instructions should tell you how long resumes remain in the database, how to update and remove your resume from the database, who has access to the database, and the fee (if any). If a database does not have specific instructions, email or call the site administrators for more information.

Some sites may require you to fill out personal information online, such as your name, email address, and resume title, but most allow you to attach your own resume, or paste it in a specific area.

When emailing your resume to a database, don't overlook one very important part of your email: the subject line. The subject line generally becomes your resume title; therefore, it's important that it gives an indication of your field and job title. Many people mistakenly type "resume" or even their name on the subject line. The subject line is typically the first information seen by employers scanning the database, and it is often the only information a recruiter will look at. For this reason, it's important to be fairly specific on your subject line. Mention your profession, experience and—since many resumes are seen by recruiters nationwide—your location. For instance, "Financial Analyst–3 Yrs. Exp.–CFA–IL." You could also mention if you are willing to relocate, "Financial Analyst–3 Yrs. Exp.–CFA–Will Relocate."

After emailing your resume to a database, try to download your resume. Once your resume is downloaded, make sure that all information is there and presented clearly. This serves a dual purpose. In addition to ensuring that your resume survived electronic transmission, you can conduct a keyword search and check that the resume turns up when appropriate. Naturally, be sure to check that downloading your resume is free before attempting this.

<u>Creating an HTML Resume and Your Own Personal Home Page</u>

One of the biggest trends right now in electronic job hunting is the use of HTML resumes, as well as individual home pages on the World Wide Web. Many job hunters are now creating resumes in hypertext markup language (HTML), the text formatting language for publishing documents on the Web. Many are also rushing to create their own home page, where potential employers can search for additional information on candidates. This is no doubt in response to the hype surrounding the Web, created in part by companies and organizations that heavily advertise their own home pages in commercial or print advertisements. Coupled with books such as this one, these advertising campaigns can leave job hunters with the impression that unless they have their own home page, their job hunt and career will be left in the dust. But before we delve into the usefulness of an HTML resume or home page, let's first discuss exactly what they are and how they are used.

An HTML resume is, quite simply, a resume written in the language of the World Wide Web. At a glance, it looks similar to a regular electronic resume. It lists the name of the job hunter, personal information, work history, and educational background. It can also contain a keyword summary, special skills, or any other information you would include in your traditional paper or electronic resume. More advanced HTML resumes can contain graphics, frames, or other special features. As mentioned earlier, you can post an HTML resume to a number of smaller databases, but of the major online resume databases, very few will accept HTML resumes. Also, an HTML document cannot be emailed, so unless an employer has World Wide Web access, your resume or home page will not be seen by prospective employers.

Creating your own home page takes HTML resumes a step further. A typical job hunter's home page will include a resume, along with graphics, and perhaps some audio, video, and samples of your work, such as drawings or writing clips. You can also include links to a former employer's or alma mater's home page (you may need to get permission from the employer or school to include the link). However, when creating your own home page, you need to be sure that your employment background is emphasized over all else. It's easy to get carried away with creating a home page full of elaborate graphics or other links, but your resume should still be the core of your home page. You can alert employers to your home page by including your URL (Uniform Resource Locator) in your traditional paper or electronic resume.

Many Web browsers, including Netscape Navigator, have sites where you can learn HTML. From Netscape's home page (**http://home.netscape.com**) choose "Tech Resources" from the Computing menu. Then, select "Web Building" from the Department menu, which will teach you the basics of HTML, and adding frames, graphics, sound, and so forth. Or, using a search engine like Yahoo!, try the keyword "HTML" to find other sites for learning the code. Your local library or bookstore should also have books available on HTML. But if you feel you are simply not up to learning a new computer language, many of the resume posting sites discussed earlier will convert your resume to HTML (some for a fee).

If you've decided to tackle HTML and have learned the basics, you can create your own home page. Many Internet providers, such as America Online, provide subscribers with the server hard disk space to create a personal home page. Check with your service for details on how to get your own space.

Now, you may be wondering if it's worthwhile for you to have your own home page or HTML resume. The answer, quite simply, is "it depends." First, remember that you can have an HTML resume without creating your own home page. And in many cases, a simple electronic resume is really all you need. Unless you're looking for a job as a Web page designer or another technical position, most companies are not concerned with an applicant's ability to create their own home page or know

HTML. At the time of this writing, having an HTML resume or your own home page simply is not as critical as having an electronic resume or a plain text resume for emailing. However, if you have the time and inclination, learning the HTML language and creating your own home page can be a valuable technical skill to have for the future.

Multimedia and Video Resumes

Instead of using a plain paper or electronic resume, you may opt for yet another approach: creating a lively multimedia or video resume that lets your true self shine through.

While similar in nature, multimedia and video resumes are actually two different types of resumes. Most often, the video shows an applicant sitting in an office or other professional setting discussing his or her background and qualifications. Video resumes are generally in the form of dialogs or "question and answer" formats, in which an off-camera participant asks the candidate questions regarding his or her background. The video itself is short; usually no longer than five minutes, or the equivalent of a three-to-five page resume.

The multimedia resume can best be described as an electronic resume with a twist—it is bursting with advances in computer technology, using graphics, scanned photographs, and sound, as well as text, to convey an applicant's background to an employer. These resumes are usually sent to an employer on disk or posted online in an online resume database. Some job seekers maintain multimedia resumes as part of their home page on the World Wide Web. A typical multimedia resume includes virtually the same information contained in a regular resume, such as a summary of qualifications, accomplishments, work history, and educational background. However, instead of having this information plainly laid out on the computer screen, a multimedia resume is interactive. A multimedia resume might have a menu or different icons that the user clicks on.

Before running out to find a friend with a video camera, a few words of caution. Multimedia and video resumes are, for the most part, fairly unusual in the world of human resources, so don't even consider permanently scrapping your traditional resume in favor of a new, high-tech version. It's best to use these types of resumes as complements to your regular resume.

However, if you are in a creative, high-tech field where knowledge of cutting-edge technology is valued, a multimedia or video resume may be effective. In fact, in some industries, a multimedia or video resume is essential in order to get noticed. A multimedia resume, for example, is practically a must if you are applying for positions in the field of multimedia technology, such as CD-ROM production or the Internet. In these fields, a multimedia resume is the easiest way to show off your skills to a potential employer. Not only will you be showing your talents to people who can appreciate them, but you can be confident that the company has the capacity to run your resume.

In television broadcasting, a form of the video resume is considered standard practice. Directors, producers, and reporters compile short videos that include information regarding their work and educational background, personal data (such as phone numbers and addresses where the candidate can be reached), as well as video clips of their best work. In fact, it's *expected* that candidates for these positions will send in video resumes, since that is the best way for the producer (or other hiring managers) to judge the quality of their work. But even if you are applying for a position where you will *not* be on the air (such as public relations), a video resume would still be appropriate, since you could be assured that whatever station you applied to has not only the equipment to easily view your video, but would appreciate it as well.

What You Need to Know Before You Use a Multimedia or Video Resume

Multimedia and video resumes are far from common in the workplace for a number of reasons:

- **Time.** Human resources departments are increasingly short-staffed, as is evident in the increasing popularity of computer scanners to "read" resumes, applicant tracking systems, and computer-assisted job interviews. Most recruiters simply don't have time to spend more than five minutes on a new applicant, as is often required by these new, high-tech resumes.
- **Equipment.** Most recruiters don't have a VCR in their office, and many recruiters, especially those in nontechnical fields, don't have the right equipment to see and hear the information on multimedia resumes. If a company doesn't have the right

equipment, your hard work could very well end up in the garbage.

- **Liability.** Many recruiters are fearful of using hiring methods where they could potentially be accused of allowing bias to affect the selection process. Recruiters can open themselves up to potential lawsuits by virtue of age, race, gender, or weight discrimination—to name a few. Multimedia resumes are also susceptible to this problem, especially those that include personal information pertaining to age, marital status, or health, or a scanned photograph of the applicant.

The best advice is to know your audience. Call the company to find out if they accept multimedia or video resumes. Finally, and most importantly, your multimedia or video presentation should be *unparalleled* in quality! After all, if recruiters take the time to look at your special resume, you'd better make sure it's worth their while.

Creating Your Own High-Tech Resumes

Multimedia Resumes

If you are planning on sending a multimedia resume on disk directly to a company, then, as with a video resume, you need to call the company to be sure that they have the capabilities to view it. When you call, you should also find out if the company primarily uses PCs or Macintosh computers. Of course, if you are planning on posting your resume online, or are planning on incorporating a resume onto your own Web page, then you will not need to do this.

If you are considering using a multimedia resume, you are probably already fairly knowledgeable about computers and have a sophisticated computer setup. But you don't need to be a computer whiz in order to create a good multimedia resume. Once you have the proper equipment, such as a sound card and scanner, you will need to decide how intricate you want to make your resume. After all, a cutting-edge multimedia resume won't do you any good if it requires such sophisticated equipment that few people would actually be able to use it. Therefore, your decision should be based upon your target audience. If you are in a nontechnical field, such as entertainment, you should try to design a multimedia resume that doesn't require all the best and latest computer equipment to view it. For a more technical position, such as a multimedia programmer, you can be more adventurous, while being relatively sure that the company you send your resume to will have the right equipment to access your resume. Keep in mind that the less complicated the resume, the more people it will be available to. This advice holds true whether you are sending a resume on a disk, posting your resume online, or creating your own Web page.

Most multimedia resumes include standard information, such as skills, experience, and accomplishments. Check out resumes posted online for ideas regarding design and content. Use plenty of icons or menus to help guide users through your resume. Don't try to make your multimedia resume *too* flashy. Your graphics should enhance, not overshadow, your accomplishments. Finally, if using links to other Websites, be careful that the content is appropriate. Bear in mind that by linking to other sites you face the risk that this will take away from, not enhance, your own resume and qualifications (you may need permission to link to some sites).

Video Resumes

If you've decided to use a video resume, you should have a particular company—and preferably a specific position—in mind. You also need to find out if your target company or companies will accept video resumes.

Once you've received a positive response, go ahead with creating the video. Call resume writing services or career counselors and ask if they produce video resumes. If they don't, they might be able to refer you to a video production company that has experience producing video resumes, or that at least specializes in business-related productions. The advantage of using a resume service is that you can also get valuable advice on what to discuss on the video. Do *not* simply try to produce your own videotape. A professional will be able to provide you with the proper lighting and equipment (and props, if necessary), as well as a high-quality tape. A resume writing service may also help you with the script-writing process for your video.

Once you have finished taping your resume, watch the tape carefully before sending it out to potential employers. Are you sitting up straight, looking directly at the camera? Do you have a pleasant, relaxed expression on your face? Does your voice sound confident and natural, not strained? If so, find a friend who will give you an honest opinion regarding your performance. When your video is up to par, it's time to send it out. And don't forget to include a paper copy of your resume; an employer will need this for their files, or to scan into their resume tracking system.

CHAPTER TWO

COMMERCIAL ONLINE SERVICES

Commercial online services offer job hunters a full range of career services, including networking resources, areas to post resumes, business databases for researching companies, and finally, job listings. This chapter will explore some of the available resources for job listings on three major commercial online services: **America Online**, **CompuServe**, and **The Microsoft Network**. And because many services provide their users with valuable, comprehensive career resources that do not include job listings, we have included those resources in this chapter as well. *However, resources devoted exclusively to resume posting, company research, and networking are described in their respective chapters.*

An Introduction to Commercial Online Services

Unlike the terms "Usenet" or "World Wide Web," which refer to specific areas of the Internet, the phrase "commercial online service" is used to describe a company that charges a fee for access to its online services. While this may sound just like an Internet service provider, there's an important difference: Internet service providers allow users to access different areas of the Internet, like Usenet or the Web. Commercial online services do this as well, but also provide access to their own resources—services that were developed especially for their subscribers.

During the 1980s, the period when most commercial services were being developed and introduced, the Internet was largely an arena for a select group of academics, scientists, and government officials. Unless you were in one of these groups, it was nearly impossible to secure Internet access. Usenet newsgroups were used mainly by computer scientists and other intellectuals, and the Web was still years away from being a reality. Commercial online services were developed in order to bring online services to the masses. These services quickly became popular because of the information and entertainment they provided—such as up-to-the minute stock quotes and interactive games. Plus, their colorful, graphic user interfaces made commercial services easy to navigate, even for users with little computer experience.

Today, commercial services remain a favorite of families and—to a lesser extent—businesses. Services like America Online are often the easiest way to learn about cyberspace. Many people, especially technical neophytes, find commercial online services less intimidating to use than the Internet. Unlike the Internet, for instance, the information on online services is well-organized and easy to find. Additionally, new users can take advantage of online tutorials and guided tours that teach new members how to use the service most effectively. Also, most services have an online member support area where users can find answers to many frequently asked questions. If they can't find an answer, they can leave a question for a member services representative. The Internet simply does not have these types of support systems for its users, which is a main reason why more than twenty million users rely on commercial online services as their main source for online information.

The Major Players

While commercial online services share a common history and purpose, and have many similarities, no two services are exactly alike. For instance, Delphi began as a text-based service without any graphics or art, while America Online relies heavily on art to enhance its service. Not all differences, however, are as marked as that. Many are different simply in terms of the services they offer. For instance, some are more entertainment-oriented while others are more business-oriented.

If you are considering subscribing to a commercial online service, you probably already have a good sense of what you are looking for in a service, whether it be entertainment, information, or easy Web access. The following is simply an overview of each service to indicate its relative strengths and weaknesses. To find out more information on how to sign up with a commercial online service, call the phone numbers listed or visit their Website. In most cases, you will receive free software that will let you try out the service free for one month, or for a specific number of hours.

- **America Online**
  800-827-6364
  http://www.aol.com
  The largest commercial online service with more than 17 million households, America Online is well-known for its wide range of home and leisure activities for the entire family. Since the creation of the online Career Center in 1989, America Online has been the leader among commercial online services in terms of the resources it offers for job hunters. America Online's employment databases contain thousands of job openings, and all use the same fairly simple search engine to access information in the databases. These job listings can all be accessed with the keyword "Career Center." Online newspapers can be found by clicking on "Local Resources"; Federal opportunities can be found by clicking on "Find a Job" and then selecting a relevant site from the WorkPlace site. America Online now offers a 4.0 version, which provides a host of new features. These offer subscribers the ability to spellcheck and put pictures in email, switch between AOL screennames without signing off, and more.

- **CompuServe**
  800-848-8990
  http://www.compuserve.com
  CompuServe was purchased by America Online in 1998, yet it remains a separate and distinct service. A large portion of CompuServe's two and a half million subscribers are businesses, which is a good indication of the service's orientation. CompuServe has by far the best collection of business

resources available online, including dozens of business-related databases. Job listings are not the primary reason most job hunters like using CompuServe. While it does have two services devoted to job listings, CompuServe Classifieds and E-Span, its strengths lie in its research capabilities and professional forums. And of course, CompuServe offers subscribers complete Internet access, including a Web browser, so subscribers can also access career-related newsgroups and Websites. Another CompuServe strength is its forums—over 700 special groups for people of like ideas and interests to gather and exchange information. CompuServe 2000 was recently released, and offers many of the features found in the new America Online 4.0. New features include the ability to spellcheck and insert pictures in email, and improved Internet capabilities.

- **The Microsoft Network**
  800-386-5550
  http://home.microsoft.com
  Known the world over for its personal computer software, Microsoft got off to a late start in the commercial online services game. However, the popularity of the company's Windows 95 and 98 operating systems has been helping The Microsoft Network (MSN) draw new subscribers. Members will want to check out its Career Forum, which features a wealth of job search and career advice, tutorials, and information. Specialized forums include those devoted to nursing and theatre professions.

Other Players

In addition to these major services, the following two services are worth mentioning here—if for no other reason than that they were once somewhat more prominent than they are today. They are as follows:

- **Prodigy**
  800-776-3449
  http://www.prodigy.com

In the past, Prodigy was best known as the favorite online service of families with young children, mainly because of its educational resources and games. But today, Prodigy's greatest asset is the easy Internet access it provides for its subscribers. Users can easily switch between Prodigy's services, the Web, Usenet newsgroups, and Gopher. Plus, Prodigy's main menu even contains some hypertext links to Prodigy-sponsored Websites. **Note:** Prodigy offers *Prodigy Classic*, which provides an impressive variety of member services, and *Prodigy Internet*, which is distinguished primarily by its faster and more complete access to the Internet, via a partnership with Microsoft's Internet Explorer. Prodigy's Career Channel is an excellent example of the service's ability to incorporate the World Wide Web into a traditional online service.

- **Delphi**
  www.delphi.com
  This service allows free access to its many forums. Searching the "Business/Finance" forums will lead you to a number of career-related forums, though few have actual job listings. These forums are best used for networking, finding the occasional job lead, or staying up-to-date with current discussions in different fields.

At one time, not all commercial online services provided subscribers with full Internet access. Commercial online services and the Internet were seen as two separate and opposing services; you either used one or the other, but not both. But the World Wide Web has opened the Internet to the general population, and today, all the major services offer complete Internet and Web access.

Another characteristic these services have in common is cost, which is traditionally the biggest drawback of commercial online services. Most commercial services recruit new members by giving away trial memberships. Services often waive their monthly fee for one month (be sure to check on specifics!), and offer up to one hundred free hours of connect time. If you exceed those free hours, however, you'll be assessed the regular hourly charge, usually about $2–$4. And of course, as soon as that free trial period is up, you immediately begin assessing charges. The monthly membership fee is usually around $20 for an unlimited usage plan. Plus, many commercial services charge additional fees for entering certain areas or accessing databases, such as CompuServe's Dun & Bradstreet's business databases.

Where to Find Job Listings and Other Career Resources

As stated before, the major commercial online resources offer a wealth of information on a wide variety of subjects. Among the information you'll find on these services are: online versions of popular magazines; up-to-the-minute news and financial information; online malls where you can shop at nationally known retail stores; discussion and interest groups dedicated to hundreds of different special interest groups; and entire volumes of encyclopedias. You can also make airline or hotel reservations, find information on different cities and restaurants, download cutting-edge software, and of course, uncover thousands of hidden job listings. It should be noted that many of these services are also available directly on the Web.

However, the job listings found on commercial online services are less extensive as those found through Usenet newsgroups or the World Wide Web. For example, Usenet has over 90,000 job listings in their newsgroups, while the Website America's Job Bank contains more than 930,000 jobs in its database. America Online's WorkPlace, which lists thousands of jobs in its "Classifieds" section, also links to several major career Websites, such as CareerMosaic and CareerPath. This opens the door to, potentially, hundreds of thousands of additional listings. At the same time, numbers aren't everything, and the job listing sites described on the following pages are well worth a visit. Additionally, all five of the commercial services mentioned provide access to Usenet and the Web, which means that users can browse those job databases as well. America Online, for one, offers links to a number of major job hunting sites on the World Wide Web through its own sites. Please see Chapter Four for a listing of related Websites.

AOL CLASSIFIEDS/ EMPLOYMENT AD BOARDS

Service: America Online

Keyword: Classifieds

Number of job listings: N/A

Types of jobs: Administrative, consulting, domestic, professional, sales, technical, and temporary

Locations of jobs: United States and some international

Frequency of updates: Daily

Search criteria available: Location; Job category Keyword

Insider tips: This site can be reached in a number of different ways, including simply going to "Find on AOL." These ads are posted by America Online members and change regularly. They can be accessed through AOL's Careers page (keyword: Careers) although they are not part of that service. A separate option allows job seekers to browse openings posted by employment agencies. **Note:** Most ads do not include a street address, and require job hunters to respond to all postings through email.

CAREER CENTER

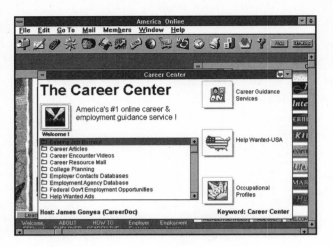

Service: America Online

Keyword: Career Center

Key features: America Online's Career Center is a comprehensive employment guide with an exhaustive library of resources for job hunters. It is one of the oldest and finest job hunting sites that can be found anywhere online. Through the Career Center, job hunters can access job listings and Talent Bank, the resume database run by Gonyea and Associates. Other key features include:

- *Career Guidance.* Includes workbook exercises to help job hunters find a satisfying career and drop-in sessions with career counselors to find answers to user's career questions.

- *Career Resources Mall.* An online mall where job hunters can purchase career-related merchandise.

- *Internship Opportunities Directory.* Contains information for thousands of paid and unpaid internships.

- *Job Hunting Advice.* Includes tips on networking, negotiating a salary or raise, and retirement planning. Job hunters will also find resume and cover letter templates, and advice on how to write a keyword resume.

- *Occupational Profiles.* Contains 250 detailed profiles of popular occupations taken from the U.S. Department of Labor publication, the *Occupational Outlook Handbook.* Users will also find a list of "hot jobs," those positions that are expected to experience higher than average growth within the next ten years.

COMPUSERVE CLASSIFIEDS

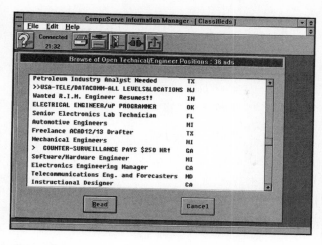

Service: CompuServe

Go: classifieds

Number of job listings: N/A

Types of jobs: All

Locations of jobs: United States and some international

Frequency of updates: N/A

Search criteria available: Job category; Posting date

Insider tips: The quality of postings in this database varies greatly. While the majority of listings are genuine employment opportunities, many are the sketchy "make money quick" or "I'm making a fortune at home" variety. The true job listings, however, are for job hunters of all levels, and include both permanent full-time and contract work. Look for job listings under "Positions Open." The classifieds also have space to post jobs and positions wanted.

E-SPAN JOB LISTINGS

Service: CompuServe

Go: espan

Number of job listings: N/A

Types of jobs: All, including banking, computers, financial, media, entertainment, science, and medical

Locations of jobs: United States and some international

Frequency of updates: N/A

Search criteria available: Job category; Location; Posting date

Insider tips: The CompuServe version of the popular job hunting World Wide Web site has more features than the version once available on America Online, but still lacks the resume database and employer profiles of the Web version. But the CompuServe site does offer some important job hunting information, like networking and interviewing tips, as well as rules and advice for writing resumes. The jobs database is divided into 17 different categories ("Internet Related Services", "Business Services/Investments", etc.) to make your job search easier.

Other Resources from Commercial Online Services

The following is a list of additional resources found on the more popular commercial online services. At the following sites, you'll find information for contacting companies, company profiles, industry trends, and much more. You'll also discover forums that are great for networking, as well as gathering company and industry information. **Note:** Many of these services assess fees in addition to the regular monthly subscription fees for the commercial online service. It's a good idea to check out the pricing information provided by each site before you enter or register with the site.

HEALTH PROFESSIONALS NETWORK

Keyword: HRS or Better Health

Choose "Health Professionals Network" from the main menu. The Network contains over seventy-five topics for all types of health professionals, including physicians, physician assistants, and physical therapists.

HOOVER'S BUSINESS RESOURCES

Keyword: hoover

Calling itself "The Ultimate Source for Company Information," Hoover provides profiles for over 13,000 international companies, including information on company officers, annual sales, and number of employees. Each company profile even allows you to search the Web for references to the specific company. You can also find information on the top fifty companies for selected U.S. cities such as Atlanta and Boston, and Los Angeles; which companies are in the *Fortune* 500; and links to over 3,500 corporate Websites. Searching the database carries no fees in addition to the connect time charges from America Online.

LEGAL INFORMATION NETWORK

Keyword: LIN

The Legal Information Network offers networking resources for paralegals, family law specialists, social security specialists, women lawyers, and law students.

PROFESSIONAL FORUMS

Keyword: places

A discussion group for professionals in all disciplines, including landscape and architecture, construction, engineering, education, financial services, and many, many more.

THE TEACHER'S LOUNGE

Keyword: teacher's lounge
Allows teachers of kindergarten through the twelfth grade to trade ideas and discuss relevant issues.

THE WRITERS CLUB

Keyword: writers
This club offers writers the opportunity to exchange information, such as how to find a publisher or secure freelance work, and offers writing workshops and advice.

CompuServe

ARCHITECTURE & BUILDING FORUM

Go: ArchBldg
Allows for discussion and the exchange of information between architectural professionals.

BROADCAST PROFESSIONALS FORUM

Go: BPForum
Allows for professionals in radio and television to share news and views about the industry.

BUSINESS DATABASE PLUS

Go: busdb
This database contains five years' worth of articles from over 750 business magazines, trade journals, and regional business newspapers. You can also find articles—dating back two years—from more than 500 specialized business newsletters. Updated weekly, this comprehensive database can provide you with timely, in-depth information on business and industry trends from throughout the world. The database also contains detailed company profiles

and industry descriptions. In addition to CompuServe charges, there's a $1 charge per article that is read or downloaded.

COMPUTER CONSULTANTS

Go: Consult

Allows computer professionals to discuss issues related to the field, including networking and business development.

CORPORATE AFFILIATIONS

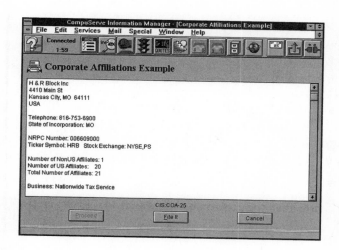

Go: affiliations

This extensive database contains company profiles for most large public and private companies worldwide and their subsidiaries. A company profile can contain an address, phone number, and description, as well as names of directors and executives, total sales, assets, net worth, liabilities, and if applicable, what exchange the company's stock is traded on. Some listings also contain the corporate family structure, parent company name and location, and more. Published by the National Register Publishing Company and made available by Dialog Information Services, Corporate Affiliations charges $4 per search, and $7.50 for a full company reference. These charges, in combination with the monthly fees from CompuServe, can add up to some pretty hefty research fees.

COURT REPORTERS FORUM

Go: Crforum

Networking forum for court reporters that includes information from the National Court Reporters Association and the *Journal of Court Reporting*.

DESKTOP PUBLISHING FORUM

Go: Dtp

Discussion group for professionals in the field of electronic publishing, design, writing, and printing.

DISCLOSURE SEC

Go: disclosure

Job hunters scanning the Disclosure database can find financial information for over 10,500 companies. The information is gathered from the 10K (annual) and 10Q (quarterly) documents that publicly traded companies are required to file with the Securities and Exchange Commission. Among the most valuable resources for a job hunter is the management discussion, which generally indicates the future direction and financial health of a company. You will also find annual income statements, balance sheets, and ratio reports (some going back as far as eight years); quarterly income statements; ownership information (including the names, holdings, and transactions of the company's principals and institutions); the letter the president sends to all shareholders; and more. Charges for reports vary, depending on how much information you want. There's no charge for a company's name and address, but it costs $4 for a company profile and $8 for a company's financial statements. However, you can get all reports, including the company profile, financial statements, management discussion, president's letter, officers, and directors, for $23.

DUN'S ELECTRONIC BUSINESS DIRECTORY

Go: dunsebd

Dun's database provides directory information on over eight million U.S. businesses and individuals, including both public and private companies of all sizes and types. Company information includes the address, telephone number, type of business, number of employees, industry, SIC code, and Dun's number. An entry for an individual most likely will not contain all this information. In addition to CompuServe's monthly fees, you'll spend $7.50 for a search that retrieves up to five companies, and an additional $7.50 for five more companies. Full company references are extra, and searches that yield no results will cost $1.

DUN & BRADSTREET ONLINE

Go: duns

Dun & Bradstreet Online contains six additional databases that yield more substantial information than what you'll find in Dun's Electronic Business Directory. These databases contain directory information on almost 12.5 million U.S., Canadian, and international companies, as well as business reports with financial information on additional companies. Again, these databases carry transaction charges in addition to the regular CompuServe fees. Charges range from $7.50 for a search of Dun's Market Identifiers, to $100 for a copy of the financial records and summary financial for a European company in Dun's Financial Records Plus Summary Financials.

- **D & B Dun's FRP History/Operations Reports.** Covers over 2.7 million publicly and privately held U.S. companies and 2.5 million Western European businesses. In addition to company names, addresses, and telephone numbers, you can find sales figures, number of employees, date of incorporation, corporate family hierarchy, and name of the chief executive. For U.S. companies, you will also find a short company history. Expect to pay $10 for your search, $50 for a full company report ($25 for a European company).
- **D & B Dun's FRP Summary/Financials Reports.** Only look at this database if you are researching European companies, because the

information for U.S. companies is the same as that found in Dun's FRP History/Operations Reports. For European companies, however, you will also find a financial summary that includes total assets, liabilities, and net worth. Again, you'll pay $10 for a search, which can yield up to five companies, and $75 for a full company report ($100 for a European company).

- **D & B Dun's Market Identifiers.** Contains information on more than ten million U.S. companies (both public and private), government organizations, and schools and universities. You'll find the name, address, and telephone number for all companies. Other information you are likely to find for most companies includes sales revenue, number of employees, net worth, incorporation dates, and names and titles of company executives and officers. Searches cost $7.50, plus another $7.50 for each full reference.

- **D & B Dun's Canadian Market Identifiers.** Information covers over 500,000 Canadian companies. Listings include name, address, telephone number, sales revenue, and name of the chief executive officer. The cost is the same as that for Dun's Domestic Market Identifiers.

- **D & B Dun's International Market Identifiers.** Contains information on over 4.7 million public, private, and government-controlled companies in Asia, Africa, Europe, the Middle East, South America, Australia, and the Pacific Rim—120 countries in all. Most entries include name, address, telephone number, cable or telex number, type of business, size (by number of employees and sales), name of the chief executive, and the parent company name. The cost is the same as that for Dun's Domestic Market Identifiers.

- **Dun & Bradstreet Business Reports.** Includes three types of financial and credit reports containing information on over ten million companies. These reports are the Business and Information Report, the Payment Analysis Report, and the Supplier Evaluation Report. The reports contain such information as the Dun & Bradstreet rating, company history, payment filings, public filings, and other financial information. While there's no charge for a search that retrieves no results, fees for successfully retrieved reports range from $45 to $360.

EDUCATION FORUM

Go: Edforum

This forum is open to teachers at all levels, administrators, college and university personnel, as well as education publishers, for the discussion of issues relevant to education.

HEALTH PROFESSIONALS NETWORK

Go: MedSIG

Open to all professionals in the health care field to discuss medical issues and exchange information regarding such topics as new advances in medicine.

INVESTEXT

Go: invtext

Here, job hunters will find in-depth reports on more than 8,200 public U.S. companies and over 2,300 public foreign corporations, as well as industry reports for over fifty industry groups, such as consumer goods and services, real estate, and finance. Compiled by fifty leading Wall Street, regional, and international brokerage houses and research firms, the reports contain company profiles and a detailed financial history including revenues, earnings, stock performance, and an analysis and projection of future performance. Costs range from $7.50 for a search by topic or report number to $20 for a report title search. Full page citations also cost $15 each.

JOURNALISM FORUM

Go: Jforum

This group is a place for journalists of all kinds—print, radio, television, even freelancers. You can discuss issues of the day, look for jobs, and talk about the business of news.

PHOTO PROFESSIONALS

Go: Photopro

Imaging professionals and all those interested in entering the field are welcome to join in a wide range of discussions regarding imaging and photography.

PROPUBLISHING FORUM

Go: Propub

Open to anyone in publishing or the graphic arts to discuss issues relating to the field. This forum charges a small monthly fee to its members.

PUBLIC RELATIONS FORUM

Go: Prsig

This discussion group for marketing and PR professionals is great for networking and finding contacts. It also offers its members a huge library of information.

THOMAS REGISTER ONLINE

Go: thomas

Thomas Register provides job hunters with profiles for almost 150,000 U.S. and Canadian manufacturers and service providers. Each record contains the company name, address, and telephone number, and the type of products or services provided. Some records also contain number of employees, names and titles of chief executives, names of parent or subsidiary companies, asset rating, and more. Searches cost $5 to retrieve up to five companies, $5 for each additional set of five companies, and $5 to view a full company record.

WRITERS FORUM

Go: Writers

Here, writers of all experience levels can make contacts, get advice, receive support, or have their work critiqued. This site is especially helpful for writers who are looking to break into freelancing.

CAREER FORUM

Go: Careers

Career Forum features career chats, answers to specific questions, and advice from experts. Job hunting tips are also available.

CHAPTER THREE

USENET
NEWSGROUPS

Usenet newsgroups are one of the oldest and most misunderstood areas of the Internet. What was once the exclusive territory of this country's brain trust—academics, scientists, and top government officials—has developed into one of the most popular means of exchanging information on the Internet. At the same time, many new users are scared off by what they perceive as an intimidating Usenet culture. But by ignoring the discussion groups on Usenet, you could miss out on hundreds of potential job opportunities.

How Usenet Newsgroups Are Structured

Quite simply, Usenet is a collection of thousands of individual discussion groups, called newsgroups, which can be accessed through a direct Internet connection or through commercial online services like America Online or CompuServe. Anyone with access may post messages to these newsgroups, which are broadcast to interconnected computer systems. In some newsgroups, the message is sent to a "moderator" for approval before broadcast. The main purpose of the moderator is to ensure that advertising on newsgroups is kept to a bare minimum. Otherwise, messages are generally left uncensored. Usenet allows millions of users worldwide to discuss any topic imaginable—sports, current events, Elvis—you name it. Because newsgroups cover such a wide range of topics, they are broken down by hierarchies, or general categories, which enable you to more easily find the topics you want. The main hierarchies are as follows:

alt. (alternative)

comp. (computers)

humanities. (arts, literature, and other humanities)

misc. (miscellaneous)

news. (news for Usenet users)

rec. (recreation)

sci. (science)

soc. (social issues)

talk. (serious discussions about often controversial
issues)

There are also dozens of local hierarchies, such as atl. (Atlanta), il. (Illinois), or swnet. (Sweden), which don't fall into any of the above hierarchies. The local hierarchies have newsgroups that cover subjects such as city politics, and some are online classifieds, with items like cars, bicycles, or kittens for sale.

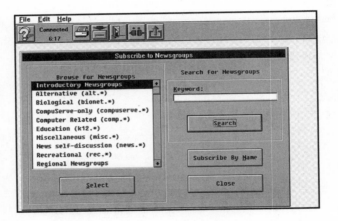

Newsgroups can be further broken down according to subject. For instance, **alt.backrubs** is in the alternative hierarchy under the subject "backrubs." And they can get even more specialized: **alt.movies.hitch-cock** and **alt.movies.monster** are in the alternative hierarchy, under the general subject "movies," discussing the movies of Alfred Hitchcock and the monster genre, respectively. Finally, each newsgroup contains discussion threads, which are basically a group of messages relating to the same topic. Every time someone posts a message regarding a new topic, a new thread is started.

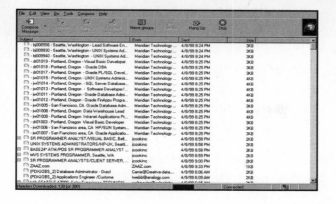

Ironically, it is this organizational and hierarchal structure that turns many people off to newsgroups. Many people open their newsreader to find a list of newsgroups, with directories and subdirectories of subdirectories, and immediately close it back up, simply because they are intimidated by what they see. They decide it's simply not worth it for them to figure out how the whole thing works, so they'll just stick with their commercial services and the World Wide Web. Unfortunately, they are missing out on a real jewel of the Internet.

How to Get Started in Newsgroups

As mentioned earlier, Usenet newsgroups are accessible either through your Internet carrier or through commercial online services. Try **Keyword: Newsgroups** in AOL. If you have a regular Internet connection, you will need the help of a newsreader, such as Trumpet Newsreader, to actually read the messages in newsgroups. A newsreader simply organizes the thousands of available newsgroups, and allows you to read and post messages. Many Web browsers, like Netscape Navigator, have a built-in newsreader. Netscape's newsreader is called simply Netscape News. If you can't find a newsreader on your system, call your Internet provider and ask where to find one.

Once you're in Usenet, you should read the messages in the newsgroups **news.newusers.questions** and **news.announce.newusers**. In these newsgroups, you'll find answers to the most commonly asked questions regarding Usenet, or you can post your own questions about Usenet. You can also find information such as a history of the Internet, rules for posting messages, and hints about the Usenet writing style.

After reviewing the basics of Usenet, post a test message to the newsgroups **alt.test** or **misc.test**. This test simply allows you to check whether your newsreader is configured properly. If you cannot post test messages, ask your Internet carrier or commercial service provider for assistance.

If your test goes off without a hitch, then you are all set. But before you begin posting messages to dozens of newsgroups on the Web, there are a few basic facts about Usenet you need to know. First, different hierarchies and newsgroups have different tones to their discussions. In general, alt. newsgroups are more casual, while the comp. and sci. newsgroups are more formal and factual. And talk. newsgroups discuss serious subjects in a serious manner. It's important to take the time to get a feel for a newsgroup. This can usually be done simply by reading a few days' worth of messages. Doing this should decrease your chances of posting an inappropriate message. *For a more complete discussion on the do's and don'ts, or "netiquette," be sure to read Chapter Eight, Networking Online.*

Using Usenet to Find Jobs

Besides being an outlet for discussions on topics as serious as politics and as frivolous as Barry Manilow, Usenet newsgroups are also one of the best sources on the Internet for job listings. Usenet has over two hundred newsgroups dedicated to job postings, each containing dozens, and often hundreds, of job listings. Some national newsgroups can even contain thousands of different job listings!

You can use job-related newsgroups to look for full-time and part-time positions, as well as short-term, contract, freelance, or consulting work. In fact, there are a number of newsgroups dedicated to postings for contractual labor. The majority of job-related newsgroups are local, but you can find plenty of national ones as well. At the time of this writing, though, most of the newsgroups researched for this book had a heavy emphasis on high-tech positions, like computers and engineering. However, this is not to say that you will not find postings for accountants or secretaries. But job hunters in less technical fields may need to look a little more carefully to find postings appropriate to their fields.

Because so many newsgroups are local and targeted toward a specific region, they are an excellent resource for job hunters interested in relocating. If you're interested in moving to another city or even another country, you can get a feel for the job market and send out your resume, without the cost of a subscription to an out-of-town newspaper.

Newsgroup job listings are also valuable because they contain more information than a traditional newspaper help-wanted advertisement. In general, these advertisements spell out the requirements for and duties of the position in great detail. One big reason for this is cost—employers, employment agencies, and professional recruiters can post job listings for free, regardless of how large or small the listing is. Few other job listing resources, whether on the Internet or in print, can say the same.

How to Instantly Search Many Newsgroups

Many of the larger job-hunting Websites, such as CareerMosaic (http://www. careermosaic.com), provide a search engine that allows you to simultaneously search more than 100 employment newsgroups for job openings. Many search engines enable you to conduct searches on the World Wide Web *or* Usenet, and Deja News (http://www.dejanews.com) is an excellent search mechanism in its own right. Deja News allows searches by specific topic, and has an extensive classifieds section. Other sites, such as JobHunt (www.job-hunt.org), do not list jobs, but do list job hunting resources, including Websites and newsgroups. JobHunt is a good place to start for those interested in searching for specific newsgroups.

Major Job Posting Newsgroups

The newsgroups listed here are specifically for the posting of jobs, but you can often find one or two job postings in a newsgroup related to your profession, so you should try to check in fairly regularly with those types of groups. For instance, if you're a veterinarian, drop in on **alt.med.veterinary**, just in case something turns up.

Note: Beware of job postings that sound too good to be true. A number of sites contain job postings with subjects along the lines of "$$MAKE MONEY AT HOME!$$" Our advice is to stay clear of those types of postings. Unfortunately, Usenet (like the rest of the online world) has its share of unscrupulous characters who try to make money off of desperate people who are looking for work.

Therefore, don't believe that simply because a job is posted on the Internet, it's legitimate.

The following list is designed to help you find job openings in your particular region or field. It should also be noted that each individual Internet provider and online service decides which newsgroups to carry; therefore, not all newsgroups will be available to everyone.

NORTHEAST/MID-ATLANTIC (UNITED STATES)

balt.jobs

Jobs available in Baltimore, Maryland.

conn.jobs.offered

Jobs available in Connecticut.

dc.jobs

Employment opportunities in Washington, DC.

ithaca.jobs

Job opportunities in the Ithaca, New York area.

li.jobs

Jobs available on Long Island, New York.

md.jobs

Jobs available in Maryland and Washington, DC.

me.jobs

Jobs available in Maine.

ne.jobs

Employment opportunities in New England.

ne.jobs.contract

Contract labor in New England.

niagara.jobs

Jobs available in the Niagara region of New York.

nyc.jobs

Employment opportunities in New York City.

nyc.jobs.contract

Contract labor and consulting opportunities in New York City.

nyc.jobs.misc

Discussion of the New York City job market.

nyc.jobs.offered

More jobs available in New York City.

nyc.jobs.wanted

Positions wanted in New York City.

pgh.jobs.offered

Jobs available in the Pittsburgh, Pennsylvania area.

pgh.jobs.wanted

Positions wanted in Pittsburgh, Pennsylvania.

phl.jobs.offered

Job opportunities in Philadelphia, Pennsylvania.

phl.jobs.wanted

Philadelphia, Pennsylvania.

SOUTHEAST (UNITED STATES)

atl.jobs

Employment opportunities in and around Atlanta, Georgia.

atl.resumes

Atlanta, Georgia.

fl.jobs

Job opportunities in Florida.

hsv.jobs

Jobs available in Huntsville, Alabama.

lou.lft.jobs

Employment opportunities in the Lafayette, Louisiana area.

memphis.employment

Employment opportunities in the Memphis, Tennessee area.

tnn.jobs

Professional job opportunities in Tennessee.

triangle.jobs

Jobs available in the Research Triangle of Raleigh, Durham, and Chapel Hill, North Carolina.

uark.jobs

Jobs wanted and available at the University of Arkansas.

us.sc.columbia.employment

Jobs available in Columbia, South Carolina.

va.jobs

Job opportunities in Virginia.

MIDWEST (UNITED STATES)

chi.jobs

Jobs available in the Chicago, Illinois area.

cle.jobs

Jobs available in the Cleveland, Ohio area.

cmh.jobs
> Job opportunities in Columbus, Ohio.

il.jobs.misc
> Discussion of the job market in Illinois.

il.jobs.offered
> Employment opportunities in Illinois.

il.jobs.resumes
> Illinois.

in.jobs
> Job opportunities in Indianapolis, Indiana.

mi.jobs
> Jobs available in Michigan.

milw.jobs
> Jobs available in the Milwaukee, Wisconsin area.

mn.jobs
> Employment opportunities in Minnesota.

oh.jobs
> Jobs available and wanted in Ohio.

stl.jobs
> Jobs available in St. Louis, Missouri.

WEST/SOUTHWEST(UNITED STATES)

austin.jobs
> Jobs available in Austin, Texas.

az.jobs
> Jobs available in Arizona.

ba.jobs.resumes
> San Francisco Bay area, California.

co.jobs
> Jobs available in Colorado.

houston.jobs.offered
> Jobs available in Houston, Texas.

houston.jobs.wanted
> Houston, Texas.

la.jobs
> Jobs available in Los Angeles, Ventura, and Orange Counties, California.

nm.jobs

Jobs available in New Mexico.

nv.jobs

Job opportunities in Nevada.

pdaxs.jobs.computers

Computer-related job opportunities in Portland, Oregon.

pdaxs.jobs.engineering

Engineering and technical job opportunities in Portland, Oregon.

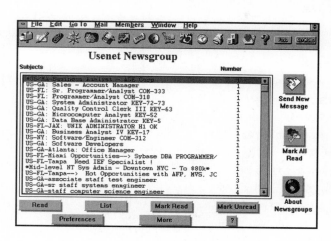

pdaxs.jobs.management

Management opportunities in Portland, Oregon.

pdaxs.jobs.retail

Retail job opportunities in Portland, Oregon.

pdaxs.jobs.sales

Sales opportunities in Portland, Oregon.

sat.jobs

Employment opportunities in the San Antonio, Texas area.

sdnet.jobs

Jobs available in San Diego, California.

seattle.jobs.offered

Job opportunities in the Seattle, Washington area.

seattle.jobs.wanted

Seattle, Washington.

tx.jobs

Jobs available in Texas.

ucb.jobs

Employment opportunities at University of California, Berkeley.

vegas.jobs

Jobs available in Las Vegas, Nevada.

wyo.jobs

Employment opportunities in Wyoming.

NATIONAL (UNITED STATES)

misc.jobs.contract

Discussion of both short- and long-term contract labor.

misc.jobs.misc

General issues of employment and careers are discussed here.

misc.jobs.offered

Job opportunities available nationwide.

misc.jobs.offered.entry

Entry-level jobs available nationwide.

misc.jobs.resumes

United States.

us.jobs

Jobs available in the United States.

us.jobs.contract

Contract labor and consulting opportunities in the United States.

us.jobs.misc

Employment opportunities in the United States.

us.jobs.offered

More employment opportunities in the United States.

us.jobs.resumes

United States.

INTERNATIONAL

ab.jobs

Job opportunities in Alberta, Canada.

aus.ads.jobs

Jobs available in Australia.

bc.jobs

Employment opportunities in British Columbia, Canada.

bermuda.jobs.offered
>   Jobs available in Bermuda.

can.jobs
>   Jobs available in Canada.

eunet.jobs
>   Job opportunities in Europe.

euro.jobs
>   More job opportunities in Europe.

ie.jobs
>   Jobs available in Ireland.

iijnet.jobs
>   Job opportunities in Israel.

kw.jobs
>   Jobs available in Kitchener-Waterloo, Canada.

ont.jobs
>   Jobs available in Ontario, Canada.

ott.jobs
>   Job opportunities in Ottawa, Ontario.

qc.jobs
>   Jobs available in Quebec, Canada.

swnet.jobs
>   Employment opportunities in Sweden.

tor.jobs
>   Jobs available in Toronto, Ontario.

uk.jobs
>   Job opportunities in the United Kingdom.

za.ads.jobs
>   Employment opportunities in South Africa.

INDUSTRY - SPECIFIC
BUSINESS SERVICES

misc.business.consulting
>   Discusses the consulting business.

COMMUNICATIONS

alt.journalism.moderated
>   Moderated discussion group for journalists.

misc.writing

> A discussion group for writers of all types.

COMPUTER

cit.jobs

> Computer-related employment opportunities nationwide.

prg.jobs

> Computer programming job opportunities available nationwide.

EDUCATION

k12.chat.teacher

> Discussion group for teachers of all grades, from kindergarten to the twelfth grade.

misc.education

> General discussion of the educational system.

GOVERNMENT

dod.jobs

> Employment opportunities with the United States Department of Defense.

LEGAL

misc.legal

> Discussion group for lawyers and others involved in the legal profession.

SCIENTIFIC/MEDICAL

alt.medical.sales.jobs.resumes

> Medical sales positions, United States.

bionet.jobs

> Job opportunities in biological science.

bionet.women-in-bio

> Discusses issues relevant to women in the field of biology.

bionet.microbiology

> Discussion of issues related to microbiology.

hepnet.jobs

> Discussion of issues relating to high-energy nuclear physics.

sci.med

Discussion group for those interested in science and medicine.

sci.med.pharmacy

Discusses the pharmaceutical field.

sci.research.careers

Discusses the various careers relating to scientific research.

sci.research.postdoc

Job opportunities in postdoctoral scientific research.

CHAPTER FOUR

THE WORLD WIDE WEB

The World Wide Web has become *the* place to look for jobs on the Internet. And with good reason. There are thousands of career resources on the Web devoted to job listings, with more springing up every day. While many contain general information regarding job hunting, a number of sites are specialized, devoting themselves to one particular field, industry, or region. Unlike Usenet newsgroups, which tend to focus on computer-related or other technical positions, the Web has listings for job hunters of all backgrounds, including those in nontraditional fields like the graphic arts and social sciences. While there is still a predominance of technical positions, the Web offers thousands of non-technical listings as well.

A Brief History of the Web

The World Wide Web came into existence in 1991, and over the past several years the general public noticed and has now embraced the Web. Before the Web, there was only the Internet—Usenet, Telnet, and Gopher—and then came the popularization of the non-Internet online services like Prodigy, CompuServe, and America Online. While the Internet was chiefly the territory of academics, government officials, and computer scientists, commercial online services became popular with families, due in large part to their user-friendly, graphical interfaces.

Although hypertext, the original concept behind the World Wide Web, was developed in the mid-1960s, its potential was not realized until almost thirty years later. Hypertext allows users to access information, such as text, graphics, or music, through predetermined links. On the Web, hypertext links are most often represented by underlined words. When a hypertext link is selected, the user is automatically transported to the linked site, which can be a completely different Web page or, as with larger sites, a file or subdirectory within the main directory. (Links may also be represented graphically, in an icon, but the results are the same as when you click on the underlined words.)

In the first few years of its existence, the Web was lightly regarded by many Internet experts, and rightly so. The Web was used almost as a new toy by computer scientists who were impressed by its graphic capabilities. Basically, the World Wide Web was interesting to look at, but offered little substantial information, so many experts dismissed the Web as a novelty that would never be a significant part of the Internet. Needless to say, they were wrong.

Many companies were quick to recognize the commercial potential of the Web. Businesses saw how the combination of graphics and text could enable them to inexpensively market their products and services to millions of potential customers, and rushed to create a home page that would allow them to do this. Now, most major companies, as well as many smaller businesses, organizations, and associations, maintain a presence on the World Wide Web.

This is not to say, of course, that the World Wide Web doesn't have its drawbacks. Many users complain that it's often difficult to find the exact information they're searching for; keyword searches using broad terms will often yield thousands of matching entries. For instance, a search using the word "cigar" can result in more than 50,000 matches! At the same time, boolean searches will narrow your search and result in fewer, but more precise, matches. But the biggest complaint most Web users have is how long it takes to download images from the Web. Even the fastest modem available can often take several minutes to download intricate graphic images from a host computer, which is often frustrating for users eager to dig in and find information.

However, most Web browsers allow you to turn off the graphics so that only the text of a Web document is received. If you have a slow modem, say 14.4 KBPS or lower, that's probably your best bet. At the same time, faster modems are beginning to make their way into the home market. Cable modems, which carry Internet access to your home through the same wires that bring you cable TV—and can carry up to ten *million* BPS—are being set up in several cities.

Despite its shortcomings, the Web has opened the Internet to commercial development, and put the Internet on the map for the general public. The main reason the Web is so popular is because it makes the Internet more user-friendly. Instead of typing in long lists of commands, users can simply point and click with their mouse, much like on the commercial online services that have been so popular for years. Today, the Web's user-friendliness and entertainment value remain its main attraction.

Like the web of a spider, the World Wide Web has no beginning and no end; it's a tangle of information that crosses and intersects. You can use hypertext links for hours without ever returning to the point at which you began. Almost any information is accessible through the Web; the paintings at the Musee D'Orsay in Paris (**http://www.paris.org/Musees/Orsay/info.html**); or the latest scores and sports news on ESPN's Web page (**http://www.espn.go.com**).

URLs Demystified

Preceding the name of any Website is a long string of seemingly indecipherable words and letters, which is called a Uniform Resource Locator (URL). While URLs are a nuisance to type in every time you want to go somewhere on the Web (forget about trying to memorize them), they are essential if you want to find any kind of information on the World Wide Web. A URL is a standardized system for finding things like files, directories, or other computers connected to the World Wide Web. Knowing what the various letters stand for helps users remember the URLs for particular sites and, as in the case with machine code identifiers, get a feel for what type of information will be found there.

Every URL must have at least two parts: a protocol and a server, or location. The protocol is simply how computers exchange information. On the World Wide Web it's called hypertext transfer protocol, since all documents on the Web are written using hypertext. The server is the name of the computer from which information is received. For instance, in the URL **http://www.vjf.com**, the server is "vjf," for the main computer at Westech Virtual Job Fair.

The United States has six basic codes to identify the type of server:

.com (commercial)
.edu (educational)
.gov (government)
.mil (military)
.org (organizational)
.net (network)

A two-letter code at the end of a location name, such as the .ie in **http://www.exp.ie**, signifies an international address (Ireland). These country codes are similar to the country codes assigned in international telephone numbers.

In addition to the protocol and server, URLs will often include a directory, subdirectory, and file name. These are simply added on to the end of a URL, and are separated by single slashes. So in the URL **http://espn.go.com/nfl/news/index.html**, "espn.go.com" is the server, "nfl" is the directory, "news" is the subdirectory, and "index" is the file name.

Where to Find Job Listings on the World Wide Web

As mentioned before, the popularity of the World Wide Web is due in large part to its user-friendly, graphical interface that makes it easier to navigate than the old, text-based Internet. One of the best examples of this fact is to compare a Usenet newsgroup such as **us.jobs** with a Web site along the lines of CareerMosaic (**http://www.careermosaic.com**). A newsgroup shows only a very long list of job openings, and it's necessary to read each individual job title to get a feel for what the job is. But with CareerMosaic, a job hunter can simply enter in his or her desired job category and location, and CareerMosaic's search engine will find jobs that match the criteria. Thus, a few clicks of the mouse produces a personalized list of jobs for specific job hunters. (Don't, however, ignore job-related newsgroups in favor of the Web. Newsgroups contain thousands of job openings that cannot be found anywhere else.)

While interesting graphics might have been what first drew job hunters to the Web, it is the veritable mountain of job-related information to be found that has kept them there. The Web has thousands of sites for job listings, and hundreds more for general job-hunting resources, such as resume banks and employer databases.

As a whole, the Web contains literally millions of job listings. It has government jobs, technical jobs, creative jobs, or entry-level jobs for new graduates, as well as permanent, temporary, and full- or part-time positions. You can find jobs in Australia, Japan, or in a state two time zones away, which is what makes the Web an especially attractive tool for anyone considering relocating.

The Web's job databases vary greatly in both the quality and quantity of job listings. We recommend starting with the all-purpose job hunting sites, such as CareerMosaic, CareerWeb, Monster.com, and HotJobs. These are four of the largest and most popular job hunting sites on the Web, and they have thousands of listings for positions in all fields, in both the United States and abroad. Each also contains other helpful career resources, such as resume databases, employer profiles, and articles and tips to help you with your job hunt. Then try some of the other sites; you will probably find a favorite or two that contains the most job listings in your field. To make things easier, don't forget to bookmark those sites where you find good information and to which you would like to return.

One advantage of scanning the Web for employment opportunities is the quality of the job listings. Some job postings on the Web run as many as 500 words, a far cry from the minuscule want ad in your Sunday newspaper. These larger ads contain detailed information about the position, such as a lengthy job description and a specific list of required experience and skills.

You may also find that a number of the listings in the major job databases overlap. The same search performed on Monster.com and CareerSite, for example, will likely retrieve many of the same listings, simply because many companies may advertise on several services at once. Be sure to keep careful records so you don't mistakenly send a resume to the same company twice for the same job listing.

In addition to the listings that follow, check out some job-related online Meta-lists, which contain additional links to thousands of other online career resources. The Career Resource Center (**http://www.careers.org**) contains thousands of links to job resources on the Web. The links are broken down into categories, like financial services, or computers and engineering. Other Meta-lists to consult include NETability Inc.'s JobHunt (**http://www.job-hunt.org**), and Purdue University's Placement Services–Sites for Job Seekers and Employers (**http://www.purdue.edu/student/job-sites.htm**). The Riley Guide (**http://www.dbm.com/jobguide**) is another superb source of job-related resources on the Web.

ADGUIDE'S COLLEGE RECRUITER EMPLOYMENT SITE

http://www.adguide.com

Number of job listings: N/A

Types of jobs: All

Locations of jobs: United States and some international

Frequency of updates: N/A

Search criteria available: Job category; Location

Resume database available: No

Employer profiles available: No

Costs for jobseekers to view jobs/ post a resume: Free; N/A

Costs for employers to list job openings/ view resumes: Prices vary – please visit the site for more information. Resumes are not available.

Other key features: Links to related sites; an **email agent** for jobseekers; links to company email addresses; financial aid information; and news and relevant articles.

Insider tips: This is a site focused on students heading into graduation, or those who have recently graduated. Recruiters post jobs to this site for entry-level through experienced positions.

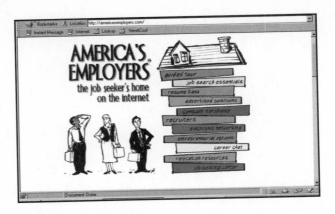

http://www.americasemployers.com

Number of job listings: 55,000

Types of jobs: High-tech, computers, engineering, medical, legal, and education

Locations of jobs: United States and some international

Frequency of updates: Daily

Search criteria available: Keyword; Company name; Job category; Location; Other (newspaper and internet ads, government listings)

Resume database available: Yes

Employer profiles available: Yes (more than 40,000)

Costs for jobseekers to view jobs/ post a resume: N/A

Costs for employers to list job openings/ view resumes: N/A

Other key features: Tips on job searching and interviewing; an employment agency database; a job search forum chat room; and the "Linkin Library," which connects jobseekers with other career-related Websites.

Insider tips: A comprehensive site with listings from Usenet newsgroups as well as newspapers.

AMERICA'S JOB BANK

http://www.ajb.dni.us
Number of job listings: More than 1 million
Types of jobs: All
Locations of jobs: United States
Frequency of updates: Daily; listings less than seven days old are starred.
Search criteria available: Job category; Keyword; Location; Job code
number; Military Occupational Code
Resume database available: Yes
Employer profiles available: Yes
Costs for jobseekers to view jobs/ post a resume: Free
Costs for employers to list job openings/ view resumes: Free
Other key features: Links to state, employer, and private agency Websites;
cover letter services; a job search resource library.
Insider tips: A joint service from the United States Department of Labor and
state employment offices, this is an immense database of jobs culled from the
combined job databases of 1,800 state employment offices. The listings
contain detailed information including a job description and educational and
work requirements. Many also contain the salary range. America's Job Bank is
also accessible through many public libraries, colleges, and universities.
Registration is required for some services. Resumes remain active for 60 days.

AMERICAN JOBS

http://www.americanjobs.com

Number of job listings: N/A

Types of jobs: All, with a focus on Hi-Tech (computers and engineering)

Locations of jobs: United States

Frequency of updates: Daily

Search criteria available: Company name; Job title; Keyword; Location

Resume database available: No

Employer profiles available: Yes

Costs for jobseekers to view jobs/ post a resume: Free; N/A

Costs for employers to list job openings/ view resumes: Job postings range from $75/posting/3 months, to $3,000 for the Corporate Platinum Package (allows a company to post an unlimited number of jobs for one year, provides a link between American Jobs and the company's home page, and places a company profile and logo at American Jobs).

Other key features: N/A

Insider tips: A good, basic career site. American Jobs claims to service 1 million queries per month, and has a growing company profiles section.

BEST JOBS USA

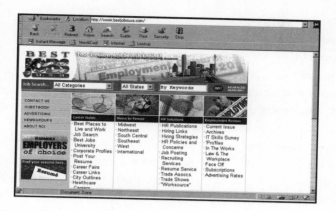

http://www.bestjobsusa.com
Number of job listings: N/A
Types of jobs: All
Locations of jobs: United States
Frequency of updates: Daily
Search criteria available: Job category; Keyword; Location
Resume database available: Yes
Employer profiles available: Yes
Costs for jobseekers to view jobs/ post resume: Free
Costs for employers to list job openings/ view resumes: N/A
Other key features: Newsgroup listings, articles from the
monthly publication *Employment Review* online, and several other career-
related resources (relocation and salary information, and more).
Insider tips: An excellent site that provides a plethora of services and
information. *Employment Review* offers a wealth of career advice to individuals
and recruiting advice to employers. There is also information about Best Jobs
Career Fairs, offered in more than 40 cities nationwide as well as links to other
employment-related sites. The site is maintained by Recourse
Communications, Inc. (RCI).

BLACKWORLD

http://www.blackworld.com/careers.htm
Number of job postings: N/A
Types of jobs: All
Locations of jobs: United States and some international
Frequency of updates: Daily
Search criteria available: Company name; Job category; Job title; Location
Resume database available: Yes
Employer profiles available: Yes
Costs for jobseekers to view jobs/ post a resume: Free
Costs for employers to list job openings/ view resumes: $160/ad/month; resumes may be accessed for $600/ six months, or $995/year.
Other key features: Jobs database; a "Business Resources" section that links you to areas such as "News", "Business Opportunities", and "Professionals"; the "Global Media" section furnishes a live audio feed from media outlets worldwide; and a link to BarnesandNoble.com, which lists a variety of helpful publications.
Insider tips: Parts of this site have been developed through a collaboration between Blackworld and CareerMosaic.

BUSINESS JOB FINDER

http://www.cob.ohio-state.edu/dept/fin/osujobs.htm
Insider tips: This site offers information on various business careers, and also has a substantial list of Websites with job and resume services.

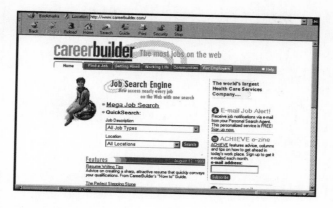

http://www.careerbuilder.com

Number of job listings: N/A

Types of jobs: All

Locations of jobs: United States and some international

Frequency of updates: Daily

Search criteria available: Job category; Keyword; Location; Salary; Skills; Type of position (full-time, part-time, contract, temporary)

Resume database available: Yes

Employer profiles available: Yes

Costs for jobseekers to view jobs/ post a resume: Free

Costs for employers to list job openings/ view resumes: N/A

Other key features: Cover letter section, career planning information and advice, links to each sponsoring company's Website, and an extensive job database.

Insider tips: CareerBuilder provides the monthly e-zine *Achieve*, which offers articles and columns about job hunting, the workplace, and starting a business. There's also a **free personal job search agent**, which allows you to use up to five search agents (so you can choose different criteria) for the same email address – you describe the job you want, and CareerBuilder notifies you when it has found it.

CAREERCITY

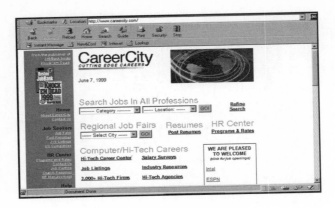

http://www.careercity.com

Number of job listings: over 31,000

Types of jobs: All, with a focus on computer and high-tech positions

Locations of jobs: United States and some international

Frequency of updates: Daily

Search criteria available: Job category and state, or keyword search by job description, job title, and country.

Resume database available: Yes

Employer profiles available: Yes

Costs for jobseekers to view jobs/ post a resume: Free

Costs for employers to list job openings/ view resumes: Rates vary

Other key features: Offers a wealth of career information from best-selling job-hunting and career books; free resume posting to a large, up-to-date resume database; and a search engine with links to over 27,000 companies featuring job listings on their Websites. CareerCity also includes information on ordering career-related books and software, and a "Feature of the Day" column with career-related articles to help you with your job search.

Insider tips: CareerCity focuses on quality professional and technical job listings. The site is a service of Adams Media Corporation, the publishers of best-selling career books such as the *JobBank* series, Martin Yate's *Knock 'Em Dead*, and this book.

CAREER.COM

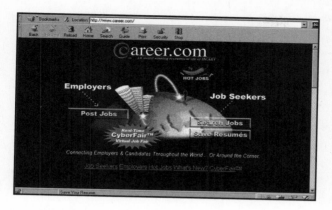

http://www.career.com

Number of job listings: 2,000

Types of jobs: All, including engineering, financial, marketing, technical, and sales

Locations of jobs: United States and some International

Frequency of updates: Daily

Search criteria available: Company; Job category; Location; Keyword

Resume database available: Yes

Employer profiles available: Yes

Costs for jobseekers to view jobs/ post a resume: Free

Costs for employers to list job openings/ view resumes: N/A

Other key features: Links to company home pages; virtual job fair; a jobs database; and special search engines for entry-level and federal job listings.

Insider tips: Career.com is good for technical positions, and the number of positions in other areas continues to grow. All the job listings contain the dates they were posted, making it easy for job hunters to gauge how long the listings have been floating around. The special area covering employment opportunities for new graduates is a great feature, as is the section featuring "Hot Jobs" of the week.

CAREER CONNECTION

http://www.connectme.com
Number of job listings: N/A
Types of jobs: All
Locations of jobs: United States
Frequency of updates: N/A
Search criteria available: Job title; Keyword; Location; Posting date
Resume database available: No
Employer profiles available: No
Costs for jobseekers to view jobs/ post a resume: Free; N/A
Costs for employers to list job openings/ view resumes: Free; N/A
Other key features: An "Advice Section" which offers tips on cover letters, resumes, and interviews; and links are offered to news and other career sites.
Insider tips: Registration is required (free).

CAREER EXCHANGE

http://www.careerexchange.com
Number of job listings: N/A
Types of jobs: All
Locations of jobs: United States
Frequency of updates: Daily
Search criteria available: Job category; Keyword; Location; Position type (part-time, full-time, contract)
Resume database available: Yes
Employer profiles available: Yes
Costs for jobseekers to view jobs/ post a resume: Free
Costs for employers to list job openings/ view resumes: A free 30-day trial was being offered at the time of this writing. Please contact Career Exchange for pricing information.
Other key features: "People-Match" email service; the "Conference Room" offers a forum for career chat; and "Relocation Tools" provides various career resources including relocation services, a salary calculator, and more.
Insider tips: Jobs posted to this site are also listed on related newsgroups and on Yahoo!Classifieds.

CAREER EXPOSURE

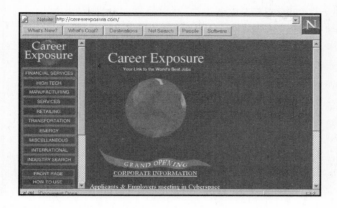

http://www.careerexposure.com

Number of job listings: N/A

Types of jobs: All

Locations of jobs: United States and some international

Frequency of updates: Daily

Search criteria available: Company name; Keyword; Location; Salary

Resume database available: Yes

Employer profiles available: N/A

Costs for jobseekers to view jobs/ post a resume: Free

Costs for employers to list job openings/ view resumes: At the time of this writing, Career Exposure was not charging employers to run job listings; however, the usual fee to list a job opening is $89 per listing.

Other key features: Thousands of job listings from major employers; links to Websites and colleges; the Biz Center, which includes the latest news, interviews, career guidance, and other related resources

Insider tips: Career Exposure is essentially a compilation of job listings at large corporate Websites, presenting those listings at its own extensive site. The quality of the listings, from a variety of well-known employers, indicates that the aim to help both employers and applicants is working. Resumes are listed on the site for four months. This site is part of the Career Exposure Network, which also includes Career Women.com, MBA Careers.com, and Diversity Search.com.

CAREERLINK USA

http://www.careerlinkusa.com
Number of job listings: N/A
Types of jobs: All
Locations of jobs: United States
Frequency of updates: N/A
Search criteria available: Job category; Keyword; Location
Resume database available: Yes
Employer profiles available: No
Costs for jobseekers to view jobs/ post a resume: Free; N/A
Costs for employers to list job openings/ view resumes: $175/posting.
Resumes may be accessed free of charge.
Other key features: Links to other career resources.
Insider tips: Careerlink USA can email jobseekers' resumes directly to
employers, or employers can conduct their own resume search.

CAREERMAGAZINE

http://www.careermag.com
Number of job listings: N/A
Types of jobs: All, but emphasis on computer-related listings
Locations of jobs: United States and some international
Frequency of updates: Daily
Search criteria available: Job category; Job title; Keyword; Location; Skills
Resume database available: Yes

Employer profiles available: Yes

Costs for jobseekers to view jobs/ post a resume: N/A

Costs for employers to list job openings/ view resumes: Employers may advertise job listings at the rate of $125/each for 42 days.

Other key features: Career-related news and articles from publications such as the *National Business Employment Weekly*, and information on networking and interview preparation. The Career Forum is moderated and discusses issues concerning the job search and the workplace. Dozens of links to other employment-related sites include salary guides and an employment agency directory. An "On Campus" section is tailored toward college students, while a "Diversity" area focuses on workplace diversity and minority opportunities.

Insider tips: CareerMagazine offers numerous other career resources to job hunters, such as the World Wide Web Resume Database and career articles. Networking opportunities include ways to post your resume directly to job fairs.

CAREERMART

http://www.careermart.com

Number of job listings: N/A

Types of jobs: All, with a focus on high-tech

Locations of jobs: United States and some international

Frequency of updates: N/A

Search criteria available: Location; Job category; Company name

Resume database available: Yes

Employer profiles available: N/A

Costs for jobseekers to view jobs/ post a resume: N/A

Costs for employers to list job openings/ view resumes: N/A

Other key features: HI-TECH, a section of this site devoted to high-tech jobseekers and employers, providing jobs and resume databases, high-tech news and chat, and more; **Email Agent**, which automatically emails you when a position that matches your search criteria turns up in the database; a resume database; links to the home pages of major employers; a newsstand where you can browse top publications such as *USA Today* and *Fortune*; and Career Chat, a forum for discussing career-related topics.

Insider tips: CareerMart features interesting, detailed graphics and valuable information for job hunters of all types. What is especially useful are the links to top employers across the country *and* to the Web pages of universities, colleges, and community colleges nationwide, which makes this site appealing to students and recent graduates. Also, its "Advise tent" section discusses industry outlooks and projections for where the job opportunities will be in the coming years.

CAREERMOSAIC

http://www.careermosaic.com

Number of job listings: N/A

Types of jobs: All, with a focus on accounting, finance, health care, and high-tech

Locations of jobs: United States and some international

Frequency of updates: Daily

Search criteria available: Job title; Company name; Location; Keyword

Resume database available: Yes

Employer profiles available: Yes

Costs for jobseekers to view jobs/ post a resume: N/A

Costs for employers to list job openings/ view resumes: $160/month/ad for job listings.

Other key features: Contains several international job databases, including International Gateway, featuring thousands of job opportunities worldwide; a searchable database of job listings from Usenet; and links to hundreds of sponsoring companies. It also includes information for college students such as job opportunities and programs (College Connection), online job fairs, and a Career Resource Center, which gives job hunting advice as well as information on industry trends.

Insider tips: Whether you're looking for job opportunities close to home or across the globe, CareerMosaic is a must-see. Job hunters of all experience levels can find advice and tips on everything from writing a cover letter to managing their career.

CAREERPATH

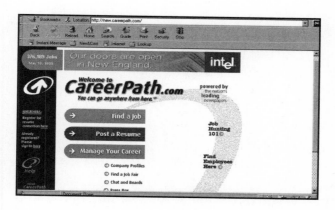

http://www.careerpath.com

Number of job listings: 350,000

Types of jobs: All

Locations of jobs: United States (newspapers from 88 major cities were represented at the time of this writing)

Frequency of updates: Daily

Search criteria available: Company name; Industry; Job Category; Keyword; Location; Newspaper name; Dates (for newspapers)

Resume database available: Yes

Employer profiles available: Yes

Costs for jobseekers to view jobs/ post a resume: Free

Costs for employers to list job openings/ view resumes: N/A

Other key features: Contains information on participating newspapers and the areas they cover, including links to each individual newspaper's home pages. Provides a Web-based job search, with more than 10,000 open positions. Also offers a career management section, offering company profiles, industry news, and more.

Insider tips: CareerPath's job database is comprised of the daily employment ads from nearly 90 major city newspapers, including *The New York Times*, *Chicago Tribune*, *The Hartford Courant*, *Boston Globe*, *Washington Post*, *Denver Post*, *Los Angeles Times*, and *Miami Herald*. Thus, the quality of the job listings will depend on the companies that placed the ads. This is a great service for anyone considering relocating to a major city, and a great resource for researching the job market in another region. The Web-based jobs database also holds a wealth of opportunity, and a more general search will definitely field better results with this database.

CAREER RESOURCE CENTER

http://cgi.pathfinder.com/fortune/careers/index.html

Number of job listings: N/A

Types of jobs: All

Locations of jobs: United States and some international

Frequency of updates: Daily

Search criteria available: Company name; Job category; Job title; Keyword; Location

Resume database available: Yes

Employer profiles available: Yes

Costs for jobseekers to view jobs/ post a resume: Free

Costs for employers to list job openings/ view resumes: $160/job posting; contact the company for resume pricing.

Other key features: Email service to notify jobseekers of new listings matching their criteria; and career-related articles.

Insider tips: This site is the result of a collaboration between *Fortune* magazine and CareerMosaic. While many of site's options are restricted to *Fortune*

subscribers, the jobs and resume databases, as well as the "View Employers" section, are open to the public.

CAREER SHOP

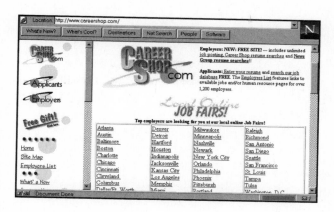

http://www.careershop.com
Number of job listings: N/A
Types of jobs: All, including professional, managerial, and technical positions
Locations of jobs: United States
Frequency of updates: Daily
Search criteria available: Job category; Keyword; Location; Posting date
Resume database available: Yes
Employer profiles available: N/A
Costs for jobseekers to view jobs/ post a resume: N/A
Costs for employers to list job openings/ view resumes: N/A
Other key features: Deja News newsgroup search engine; an
email service that notifies you of new openings that meet criteria you specify; links to national and local job fairs; and training and certification programs.
Insider tips: A good resource for jobseekers and employers alike. This site is easy to navigate, and the email service is beneficial to those who can't spend hours surfing the Web.

CAREERSITE

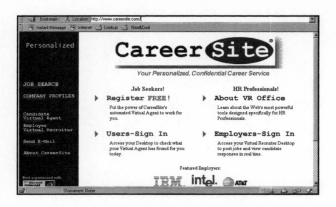

http://www.careersite.com

Number of job listings: N/A

Types of jobs: All

Locations of jobs: United States

Frequency of updates: Daily

Search criteria available: Industry; Job category; Location; Skills; Willingness to travel

Resume database available: Yes (175,000)

Employer profiles available: Yes

Costs for jobseekers to view jobs/ post a resume: Free

Costs for employers to list job openings/ view resumes: Prices and plans vary. Contact the site for more information.

Other key features: Links to company profiles and job openings for specific companies. By filling out "MyProfile," you get free access to the jobs database, **email notification** of job openings you'd be interested in, and you can post an "anonymous profile" that can be viewed by potential employers.

Insider tips: CareerSite is a unique jobs database for job hunters, and also provides services for employers. You must register in order to use some of the services. The detailed job listings include information on job requirements and qualifications.

CAREERWEB

http://www.careerweb.com

Number of job listings: N/A

Types of jobs: All fields and experience levels, covering professional, technical, and managerial jobs

Locations of jobs: United States

Frequency of updates: Daily

Search criteria available: Company name; Job category; Keyword; Location

Resume database available: Yes

Employer profiles available: Yes

Costs for jobseekers to view jobs/ post a resume: N/A

Costs for employers to list job openings/ view resumes: N/A

Other key features: JobMatch, a personalized automated database search; and career assessment tests (found under "Career Inventory"); tons of career-related resources, including links to affiliates and other job sites, plus tips and advice on internships and resume writing, the job hunt, and more; also offers books, software, and videos to help you with your job search.

Insider tips: CareerWeb is packed with information and resources for job hunters. If you register your resume, you can respond to advertisements with a simple click of a button. Also, check out the Career Doctor for columns on finding a job, self-employment, and more.

CAREER WOMEN

http://www.careerwomen.com
Number of job listings: N/A
Types of jobs: All
Locations of jobs: United States
Frequency of updates: N/A
Search criteria available: Company name; Job category; Keyword; Location; Salary
Resume database available: No
Employer profiles available: Yes
Costs for jobseekers to view jobs/ post a resume: Free; N/A
Costs for employers to list job openings/ view resumes: $89/posting. A free trial was being offered at the time of this writing. Resumes are not available.
Other key features: Links to news and resources for professional women.
Insider tips: Check out the site's advice and survey areas for more helpful information.

CAREERS.WSJ.COM

http://www.careers.wsj.com
Number of job postings: N/A
Types of jobs: All
Locations of jobs: United States
Frequency of updates: Two times per week
Search criteria available: Company name; Industry; Job category; Keyword; Location; Salary; Skills; Degree/Level of experience
Resume database available: No
Company profiles available: Yes
Costs for jobseekers to view jobs/ post a resume: Free; N/A
Costs for employers to list job openings/ view resumes: There is a fee to list job openings. Either visit the Website, or call 214/640-7869 for more details. Resumes are not available.
Other key features: Loads of career resources, including salary information, career columns, and links to executive recruiters; an **email service** that notifies the jobseeker of new opportunities and information; and links to career publications available through Amazon.com.

Insider tips: An informative site backed by the reputation of *The Wall Street Journal*. The jobseeker can search all companies in the site's database, or pick specific companies to search, such as AT&T, Anderson Consulting, Dow Jones & Co., and others.

CLASSIFIEDS2000

http://www.classifieds2000.com
Number of job listings: 200,000
Types of jobs: All
Locations of jobs: United States
Frequency of updates: Daily
Search criteria available: Company name; Job category; Keyword; Location
Resume database available: Yes
Employer profiles available: Yes
Costs for jobseekers to view jobs/ post a resume: Free
Costs for employers to list job openings/ view resumes: Ads from businesses or companies are $75/ 4 weeks (placed on more than 70 major Websites); "Domestic Jobs" postings are free.
Other key features: "Cool Notify" email service informs jobseekers of new postings matching their criteria; and a special section detailing opportunities with more than 300 start-ups.
Insider tips: An overall good jobsearch resource including more than 7,000 company profiles.

CLASSIFIED WAREHOUSE

http://www.adone.com
Number of job listings: 115,000
Types of jobs: All
Locations of jobs: United States
Frequency of updates: N/A
Search criteria available: Job category; Job title; Location; Skills; Experience level; Keyword
Resume database available: No
Employer profiles available: N/A
Costs for jobseekers to view jobs/ post a resume: Free; N/A
Costs for employers to list job openings/ view resumes: N/A

Other key features: "AdHound" email service notifies jobseekers of new ads that match their criteria.

Insider tips: Classified Warehouse includes ads for employment, autos, real estate, and more. The employment ads are taken from several local/regional newspapers across the U.S., so ad rates depend on which newspaper an employer initially places the ad in. A good site for finding local job listings, but make sure to check the date of the listing – some ads we found had been posted for more than two months.

COLLEGE GRAD JOB HUNTER

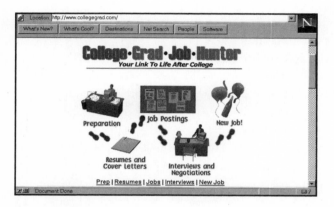

http://www.collegegrad.com

Number of job listings: N/A

Types of jobs: Internships; Entry-level; Professional

Locations of jobs: United States and some international

Frequency of updates: Daily

Search criteria available: Job category; Keyword

Resume database available: No (links to CareerCity, which has a resume database)

Employer profiles available: Yes

Costs for jobseekers to view jobs/ post a resume: Free

Costs for employers to list job openings/ view resumes: N/A

Other key features: Job Hunter e-zine offering career advice,

Insider tips: An attractive, well-organized site geared toward recent college graduates, offering a step-by-step guide to getting a job, everything from resume preparation to interviewing tips and negotiating an employment offer.

Information is adapted directly from the book of the same name; which is currently available at this site. Actual job listings are limited, but those that are available are ideal for entry-level candidates, and major employers such as Intel Corporation and Netscape detail their internship programs here. There are also links to a variety of other job hunting Websites. This site is an excellent choice for those new to the job market, while also providing opportunities for recent grads with experience. Experienced jobseekers are linked to CareerCity which, in addition to thousands of job listings, includes a resume database and other career resources.

CONTRACT EMPLOYMENT
WEEKLY

http://www.ceweekly.com

Number of job listings: 4,500

Types of jobs: Contract technical, information technology, and engineering positions

Locations of jobs: United States

Frequency of updates: Hourly

Search criteria available: Keyword; Posting date; Company name; State; Region; Country.

Resume database available: Yes

Employer profiles available: N/A

Costs for jobseekers to view jobs/ post a resume: You need to be a subscriber to access the entire database; only a portion of the database is available to nonsubscribers (U.S. subscription rates vary from $35.00/year for the electronic format to $65.00/year for the print version).

Costs for employers to list job openings/ view resumes: N/A

Other key features: Contains links to companies that regularly hire contract technical employees. Electronic subscriptions are available, as well as a resume service that mails your resume to employers.

Insider tips: This electronic version of *Contract Employment Weekly* has listings for thousands of short- and long-term technical positions. This site should be a definite for anyone looking for technical contract work, since it boasts that the advertised positions generally pay higher than other nonpermanent work.

COOL WORKS

http://www.coolworks.com

Number of job listings: 70,000

Types of jobs: Primarily seasonal employment at national parks, resorts, camps, and ski areas

Locations of jobs: United States

Frequency of updates: Weekly

Search criteria available: Job category; Location

Resume database available: No

Employer profiles available: Yes

Costs for jobseekers to view jobs/ post a resume: Free; N/A

Costs for employers to list job openings/ view resumes: N/A

Other key features: Information about volunteer opportunities, links to more than 70,000 job listings, and career placement information concerning recreational employment.

Insider tips: Cool Works does a good job of covering a unique market, that of seasonal employment. Links to colleges and various large career sites enable job hunters with an interest in these kinds of jobs to get a good glimpse of what is available. Job seekers can look at opportunities at famous national parks such as Yellowstone, Mesa Verde, and Grand Teton, among others. Partnered with the Great Outdoor Recreation Pages (GORP), an organization focusing on outdoor recreation.

E-SPAN'S JOBOPTIONS

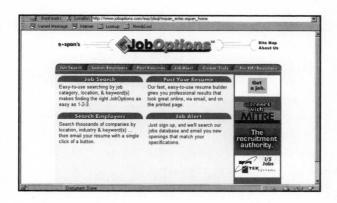

http://www.joboptions.com

Number of job listings: 10,000

Types of jobs: All, with an emphasis on managerial, technical, and professional

Locations of jobs: United States and some international

Frequency of updates: Daily

Search criteria available: Job category; Keyword; Location

Resume database available: Yes (nearly 150,000)

Employer profiles available: Yes (6,000 employers and recruiters)

Costs for jobseekers to view jobs/ post a resume: Free

Costs for employers to list job openings/ view resumes: Rates start at $150/ad for sixty days, and climb to $5,370 for an annual unlimited plan. Please visit the site for full details.

Other key features: More than enough employer profiles to keep you busy for awhile; "HR Tools" covers a variety of human resource topics; **email services for both the jobseeker *and* the employer** – "Job Alert" notifies jobseekers of new positions matching their criteria, while "Resume Alert" emails a list of possible candidates matching an employer's openings; and the "Career Tools" section offers tips on creating a resume, salary and relocation information, career news, and more.

Insider tips: Another very useful site, which is easy to navigate, and offers more than simple jobs and resume databases. Especially unique to this site is its emphasis on serving both the jobseeker and the employer, making this a must see site for people on both sides of the job search.

4WORK

http://www.4work.com
Number of job listings: N/A
Types of jobs: All
Locations of jobs: United States
Frequency of updates: Daily
Search criteria available: Keyword; Location; Job type
Resume database available: No
Employer profiles available: No
Costs for jobseekers to view jobs/ post a resume: Free; N/A
Costs for employers to list job openings/ view resumes: Jobs may be posted at the rate of $50 for the first month (unlimited posting); $20 each additional month. Volunteer opportunities and internships are posted free of charge to employers. This site does not include resumes.

Other key features: Includes job databases of regular full-time positions, volunteer positions, internships, and part-time positions , and an interactive agent that automatically matches job seekers with job listings. Also contains information on relocating, as well as links to numerous colleges and universities.

Insider tips: While it doesn't have the additional career resources (such as employer profiles and a resume database) offered by Monster.com, 4WORK's jobs database is well worth the time of the search. Or better yet, if you register your personal profile—name, email address, skills—**Job Alert!** lets you know that an employer has posted an appropriate opportunity.

HEADHUNTER.NET

http://www.headhunter.net

Number of job listings: 260,000

Types of jobs: All

Locations of jobs: United States and some international

Frequency of updates: Daily

Search criteria available: Job category; Keyword; Location; Salary; Skills; Job type (contract, full-time); Education/Experience

Resume database available: Yes

Employer profiles available: Yes

Costs for jobseekers to view jobs/ post a resume: Free

Costs for employers to list job openings/ view resumes: Free; VIP Resume Reserve: $700/ 3 months, or $1,500/ year.

Other key features: VIP Resume Reserve allows companies to view newly-posted resumes seven days before they are seen by the general public. Jobseekers can choose to either leave their resume in the VIP area permanently, or make it visible to the public seven days after posting. Resume and job postings may be updated free of charge, allowing them to be listed as new postings.

Insider tips: Because this site's job and resume posting and searching services are free (VIP Resume Reserve being the exception), Headhunter.net is a popular job site that offers a wealth of information.

THE HELP-WANTED.NETWORK

http://www.help-wanted.net
Number of job listings: N/A
Types of jobs: All
Locations of jobs: United States and some international
Frequency of updates: Daily
Search criteria available: Keyword; Posting date; With or without abstracts
Resume database available: Yes
Employer profiles available: No
Costs for jobseekers to view jobs/ post a resume: Free
Costs for employers to list job openings/ view resumes: Listings come from newsgroups and related Websites. Resumes may be viewed free of charge.
Other key features: "Other Resources" section links you to a limited number of career Websites, including JobBank USA.
Insider tips: A great way to access newsgroup listings. This is not a large site, but claims it can offer access to 2.5 million job listings.

HOT JOBS

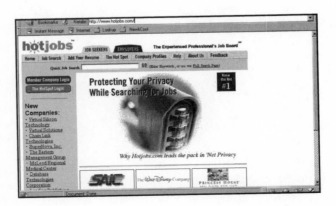

http://www.hotjobs.com
Number of job listings: N/A
Types of jobs: All
Locations of jobs: United States
Frequency of updates: Daily

Search criteria available: Keyword; Company name; Job category; Location

Resume database available: Yes

Employer profiles available: Yes

Costs for jobseekers to view jobs/ post a resume: N/A

Costs for employers to list job openings/ view resumes: $600/month (includes up to 20 concurrent postings) to $1200/month (includes up to 80 concurrent postings).

Other key features: A resume writing workshop; a **job search agent**; a message board; a "shopping cart" feature that allows jobseekers to save job announcements; and links to company home pages.

Insider tips: A growing and fairly straightforward jobs database that concentrates on jobs and companies—no career tips or unusual features. Ideal for those who want to get right to the employment opportunities.

INTERNET CAREER CONNECTION

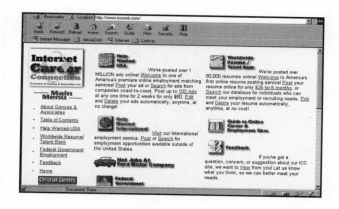

http://www.iccweb.com

Number of job listings: N/A

Types of jobs: All

Locations of jobs: United States and some international

Frequency of updates: Daily

Search criteria available: Keyword; Location

Resume database available: Yes

Employer profiles available: No

Costs for jobseekers to view jobs/ post a resume: No charge to view jobs. $25/six months to display resume.

Costs for employers to list job openings/ view resumes: $75/ad for 14 days (listed on this site and on America Online's Career Center). Other pricing plans are available. There is no charge to search resumes.

Other key features: Federal job information, and links to other career Websites.

Insider tips: This site is a provided by Gonyea & Associates, Inc. The information at this site is also located at America Online's Career Center. Unlike many of the other online career services, such as Monster.com or CareerPath, jobseekers will pay to list their resume on this site, yet the lower ad rates and broad exposure attract many large employers to the site.

THE INTERNET
JOB LOCATOR

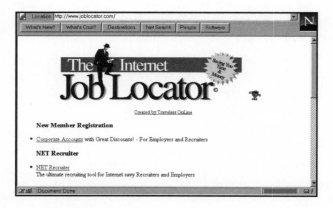

http://www.joblocator.com
Number of job listings: N/A
Types of jobs: All
Locations of jobs: United States
Frequency of updates: Daily
Search criteria available: Keyword; Company name
Resume database available: Yes
Employer profiles available: N/A
Costs for jobseekers to view jobs/ post a resume: Free
Costs for employers to list job openings/ view resumes: From $25 for

four months (includes 25 job postings and 25 resume credits) to $225 for one year (includes 300 job postings and 300 resume credits). Please refer to the "Corporate Accounts" section of this site for more details.

Other key features: Includes a jobs database which allows employers and recruiters to post jobs to appropriate Usenet newsgroups through Deja News; an **email system** that notifies jobseekers of new openings in their field; and links to other job listing sites, including CareerMosaic, and the JobHunt Meta-list.

Insider tips: As its name indicates, this site is strictly devoted to job listings. It also has links to other job hunting sites which open up thousands of additional job possibilities.

THE INTERNET JOB SOURCE

http://www.statejobs.com

Number of job listings: N/A

Types of jobs: All (openings with major companies, as well as State and Federal opportunities)

Locations of jobs: United States

Frequency of updates: N/A

Search criteria available: Keyword; Location

Resume database available: No

Employer profiles available: Yes

Costs for jobseekers to view jobs/ post a resume: Free; N/A

Costs for employers to list job openings/ view resumes: $60/posting for 60 days. Please visit the site for information on other payment plans. No resumes are listed at this site.

Other key features: 43 state and area job source pages; link to *Fortune* 500 jobs; Federal and State job listings; career-related news articles; links to major search engines and local/regional/national online news publications; and a free, weekly, online newsletter.

Insider tips: A good site to visit if your job search is focused largely on location or government positions. The newspaper and magazine listings are great for accessing current news, be it focused on your career or getting local information on an area in which you'd like to live and work.

THE INTERNET'S EMPLOYMENT RESOURCE

http://www.tier21.com

Number of job postings: N/A

Types of jobs: All

Locations of jobs: United States and some international

Frequency of updates: N/A

Search criteria available: N/A

Resume database available: No

Employer profiles available: Yes (1,300)

Costs for jobseekers to view jobs/ post a resume: Free access to other career Websites, where you can search for jobs; resumes can also be posted at linked Websites, or you can pay to have your resume submitted to this site's "resume partners." Prices for this resume service range from $14.50 to $29.50.

Costs for employers to list job openings/ view resumes: Job listings are linked from other sites. Resumes can be emailed to employers free of charge (registration required).

Other key features: An **email service** (Jobs Direct) which notifies you of openings matching general career categories or geographic regions; links to some of the Web's most popular and useful career sites; and a "Resource Library."

Insider tips: This is a good site for those who don't have the time to surf around to different Websites. The Internet's Employment Resource searches sites such as CareerMosaic and CareerPath.

JOBBANK USA

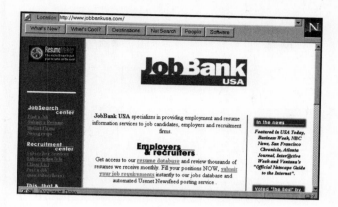

http://www.jobbankusa.com

Number of job listings: N/A

Types of jobs: All

Locations of jobs: United States

Frequency of updates: Daily

Search criteria available: Keyword; Location; Job type (permanent, contract, temporary, summer, internship)

Resume database available: Yes

Employer profiles available: N/A

Costs for jobseekers to view jobs/ post a resume: There is no charge to view jobs or post a resume. This site also offers "Resume Broadcaster" which, for an $89 fee, will send your resume to companies (more than 2,000 at the time of this writing) based on your preferences.

Costs for employers to list job openings/ view resumes: The rate for posting an ad is $125/ad for 60 days.

Other key features: Includes a jobs database; **"JobScout" (a job search e-mail service)**; career fair information; Usenet job-related newsgroups search; an online newspaper that features tips and job openings for international job hunters; and the Jobs Meta Search Page.

Insider tips: The real draw of this site is its Jobs Meta Search Page. Not only can you search the JobBank USA database, but you can perform searches in the databases of several of the major World Wide Web job hunting sites, such as Monster.com, CareerCity, and E-span's JobOptions. Of course, if you use only this service you'll miss out on the other valuable information these

services provide, but if you're short on time and only want to check out job listings, JobBank USA is an excellent choice.

JOBDIRECT

http://www.jobdirect.com
Number of job listings: N/A
Types of jobs: Entry-level for all industries
Locations of jobs: United States
Frequency of updates: Daily
Search criteria available: Education level
Resume database available: Yes
Employer profiles available: N/A
Costs for jobseekers to view jobs/ post a resume: Free; however, JobDirect members may only search job listings once they post a resume with the service.
Costs for employers to list job openings/ view resumes: N/A
Other key features: Free resume database that notifies you of job opportunities that match your qualifications and criteria.
Insider tips: Focuses on recent and imminent college graduates, and matches resumes with entry-level job openings.

JOBEXCHANGE

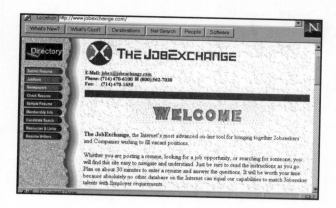

http://www.jobexchange.com

Number of job listings: 25,000

Types of jobs: All, including general labor and office support

Locations of jobs: Nationwide, including: New Jersey, Ohio, Oregon, Pennsylvania, Washington, and Wisconsin.

Frequency of updates: Daily

Search criteria available: Newspaper; Job title; Keyword; Date

Resume database available: Yes

Employer profiles available: N/A

Costs for jobseekers to view jobs/ post a resume: Free (there is a $15 fee if you choose to have JobExchange post your resume for you). Options, such as video and still photos, may be added to the online resume for an additional fee. Resumes may also be posted for 12 months for $200, which includes a resume, video or audiotape, one photo, three letters of recommendation, and three award recognitions. Please visit the site for more details.

Costs for employers to list job openings/ view resumes: Employers can browse resumes free of charge. $22 to download a resume (rates vary).

Other key features: Links to other sites and meta lists; and a career resource center.

Insider tips: JobExchange is a good example of a site that provides newspaper classifieds online. While obviously smaller than CareerPath, it does offer job seekers hoping to relocate to these areas of the country some welcome information. **Note:** Newspapers listed at this site sometimes vary. For example, newspapers from S. Carolina and Illinois had been listed previously, and have now been replaced by Oregon.

JOBFIND.COM

http://www.jobfind.com
Number of job listings: N/A
Types of jobs: All
Locations of jobs: United States
Frequency of updates: N/A
Resume database available: Yes
Employer profiles available: Yes
Search criteria available: Job category; Job title; Keyword; Location
Costs for jobseekers to view jobs/ post a resume: Free
Costs for employers to list job openings/ view resumes: $100/month/listing, and $75/month/each additional listing. There is a fee to search resumes.
Other key features: Listing of job fairs; jobs database; job listings include work schedules for openings (ex. M–F, 8:00 a.m.–5:00 p.m.); and current, related news articles.
Insider tips: Check the dates of listings you find on Jobfind.com – we found listings that had been open for several months. For those postings, you may want to contact the hiring organization to verify availability.

JOBHUNT

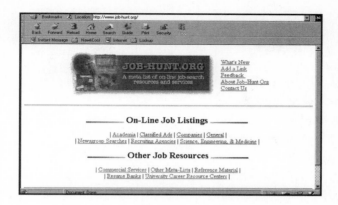

http://www.job-hunt.org

Number of job listings: N/A

Types of jobs: All

Locations of jobs: United States and some international

Frequency of updates: More than once per week

Search criteria available: N/A

Resume database available: No

Employer profiles available: Yes

Costs for jobseekers to view jobs/ post a resume: Free

Costs for employers to list job openings/ view resumes: N/A

Other key features: Search online resume banks, newsgroups, company profiles, and jobs specifically in academics, medicine, science, and engineering;
searchable database of recruiters; links to University career centers; links to
online reference material and most (if not all) of the major, most informative
career resources on the Web.

Insider tips: We found this to be one of the most thorough and complete
career sites on the Web. This site doesn't actually have jobs or resume databases, but the number of links to Websites with those resources is amazing. As
mentioned above, this site has a very respectable company profiles database
and lots of research tools, which will benefit anyone from the entry-level sales
person to the seasoned CEO.

JOB RESOURCES BY U.S. REGION

http://www.wm.edu/csrv/career/stualum/jregion.html
Number of job listings: N/A
Types of jobs: N/A
Locations of jobs: United States
Frequency of updates: N/A
Search criteria available: Location
Resume database available: N/A
Employer profiles available: N/A
Costs for jobseekers to view jobs/ post a resume: N/A
Costs for employers to list job openings/ view resumes: N/A
Other key features: No jobs database; summer job information, post graduate and internship links; and extensive salary information.
Insider tips: This site is a service of the College of William & Mary. There are no job listings or resume databases at this site, rather you may choose a region of the U.S. to get a list of links to career Websites devoted (at least in part) to that specific region. You may further break down your search by state, or search a list of national sites. This site is a good resource for those jobseekers focused on location.

JOBS.COM

http://www.jobs.com
Number of job listings: N/A
Types of jobs: All
Locations of jobs: United States
Frequency of updates: Daily
Search criteria available: Job category; Job title; Location; Job type (full-time, part-time, temporary, contract)
Resume database available: Yes
Employer profiles available: Yes
Costs for jobseekers to view jobs/ post a resume: Free
Costs for employers to list job openings/ view resumes: $99/posting for 30 days. Unlimited access to the resume database for 30 days costs $495, which also includes the site's Resumail Recruiter 4.0 software.
Other key features: A special section for student jobseekers that includes internships and entry-level jobs; access to Resumail software; and more.

Insider tips: Formerly the Resumail Network, this site is based on the Resumail software program. It claims to simplify the process of creating an online resume by allowing jobseekers to write in their information (experience, education, etc.) and the software automatically plugs it into electronic format – so employers are sure to get a readable electronic resume. Both jobseekers and employers must download the software from the site to either post a resume or read resumes.

JOB-SEARCH-ENGINE

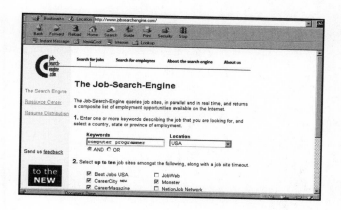

http://www.jobsearchengine.com
Number of job listings: N/A
Types of jobs: All
Locations of jobs: United States and some international
Frequency of updates: N/A
Search criteria available: Keyword; Location
Resume database available: No
Employer profiles available: No
Costs for jobseekers to view jobs/ post a resume: Free; N/A
Costs for employers to list job openings/ view resumes: N/A
Other key features: "Resource Center" lists and links to several jobs sites, career services sites, and career-related newsgroups.
Insider tips: This is a great site for collecting job listings you're interested in from all over the Web. By doing a search for keywords "computer programmer" in the US, for example, and choosing up to ten of the major career

sites listed on Job-Search-Engine, we received more than 4,000 listings from the ten sites we chose (**Note:** the 4,000 listings were not necessarily unique listings).

JOBTRAK

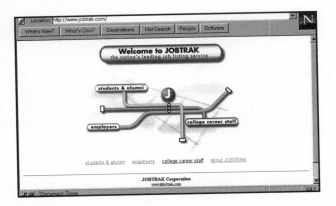

http://www.jobtrak.com
Number of job listings: N/A (3,000 new listings each day)
Types of jobs: All
Locations of jobs: United States
Frequency of updates: Daily
Search criteria available: N/A
Resume database available: Yes
Employer profiles available: N/A
Costs for jobseekers to view jobs/ post a resume: Free; however, to view job listings from a particular campus, you must be a student or alumnus of that institution.
Cost for employers to list job openings/ view resumes: Varies
Other key features: Information from colleges and career centers; a career forum; graduate school information; and a calendar of career fairs.
Insider tips: Jobtrak's primary distinction is that its job listings are geared directly toward college students, MBA's, and alumni through college career centers. Jobtrak has formed partnerships with more than 800 college and university career centers, MBA programs, and alumni centers nationwide, to bring information from these sources to job seekers.

JOBVERTISE

http://www.jobvertise.com
Number of job listings: N/A
Types of jobs: N/A
Locations of jobs: United States and some international
Frequency of updates: N/A
Search criteria available: Job title; Keyword
Resume database available: No
Employer profiles available: Yes
Costs for jobseekers to view jobs/ post a resume: Free; N/A
Costs for employers to list job openings/ view resumes: Free; N/A
Other key features: Links to other career sites, and links to communities and companies using Jobvertise.
Insider tips: Companies use Jobvertise's free service to set up a jobs page on their own homepages. The Jobvertise site can be searched for jobs coming from those homepages, or jobseekers can be directly linked to the homepages.

JOBWEB

http://www.jobweb.com
Number of job listings: N/A
Types of jobs: All
Locations of jobs: United States and some international
Frequency of updates: Daily
Search criteria available: Keyword; Location; Job type (full-time, part-time, internship, seasonal, federal, or co-op)
Resume database available: No
Employer profiles available: Yes
Costs for jobseekers to view jobs/ post a resume: Free; N/A
Costs for employers to list job openings/ view resumes: Rates vary from $80/ month for an unlimited number of postings, to $2,600/ month for a custom banner on JobWeb's homepage. Please visit the site for more details. Resumes are not available on this site.
Other key features: Extensive links to other job listing sites, newsgroups, and headhunters/search firms; information on internships and federal job postings; a searchable databases of over 1,000 career fairs, and a database of U.S. school districts; career planning resources; special opportunities for minorities and job

hunters with disabilities; and the "Job Search & Industry Information" section containing dozens of links to business sites like Dun & Bradstreet's Economic Analysis & Trends page, and a site listing the *Fortune* 500.

Insider tips: JobWeb is truly a Web of useful information, with more than 100 links to other job hunting resources. JobWeb's employer directory offers detailed information, and the JobPlace discussion forum is a great way to exchange job search and career information.

THE LATPRO PROFESSIONAL NETWORK

http://www.latpro.com
Types of jobs: All
Locations of jobs: United States and some international
Search criteria available: Job category
Resume database available: Yes
Employer profiles available: No
Insider tips: All jobs on this site require the jobseeker to be fluent in Spanish and/or Portuguese.

MBA FREEAGENTS.COM

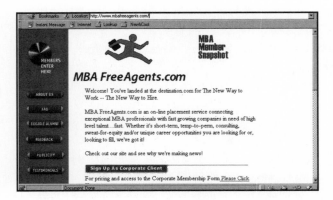

http://www.mbafreeagents.com
Number of job listings: N/A
Types of jobs: Interim, high-tech and business-related jobs for MBAs
Locations of jobs: United States and some international
Frequency of updates: Daily

Search criteria available: Keyword; Job type; Company name

Resume database available: Yes – alumni members database

Employer profiles available: N/A

Costs for jobseekers to view jobs/ post a resume: N/A

Costs for employers to list job openings/ view resumes: N/A

Other key features: Job listings, email interaction between job seekers and employers/hiring managers, and a database of alumni members (5,000 as of March 15, 1999).

Insider tips: Membership is required for this job matching service for experienced MBAs from top business schools. The 39 schools included (Carnegie Mellon, Harvard Business School, and many others) are all members of the International MBA placement group. According to the service, the majority of applicants meet one of the following criteria—one to fifteen years out of business school, thirty years of experience, or an independent consultant who goes from one job to the next—so clearly, this site is not for all job seekers. However, it is a good example of a job hunting Website that focuses on a target audience and succeeds at it. Job seekers who qualify should register in the alumni members database, which is searched by employers and hiring managers.

MONSTER.COM

http://www.monster.com

Number of job listings: 210,000

Types of jobs: All

Locations of jobs: United States and some international

Frequency of updates: Daily

Search criteria available: Industry; Job category; Keyword; Location

Resume database available: Yes

Employer profiles available: Yes

Costs for jobseekers to view jobs/ post a resume: Free

Costs for employers to list job openings/ view resumes: $225 per posted ad for 60 days. There is a fee for viewing resumes.

Other key features: "Zones" for different experience levels and specific fields (such as Health care); expert job hunting and career advice; a **job search agent**; and links to other career sites. There are also links to international sites like Monster Board UK.

Insider tips: Monster.com (formerly The Monster Board) is one of the best (and best known), most comprehensive job-hunting resources on the Web. It's an easy-to-use, graphically entertaining site that provides job hunters with tons of valuable information. The job listings themselves are thorough and if you have previously submitted your resume to the resume database, you can apply for positions with impressive ease. It's a true monster, too, growing all the time through partnerships with other job-hunting sites. **Note:** Two sites we profiled in the previous edition of this book, Medsearch (now monster Healthcare) and Online Career Center, have since been acquired by Monster.com.

NATIONAL OPPORTUNITY NOCS

http://www.opportunitynocs.org

Number of job listings: 450

Types of jobs: Nonprofit including: arts, social services, education, health, public sector; many openings for executives, managers, and administrators

Locations of jobs: United States

Frequency of updates: Daily

Search criteria available: Keyword; Location; Posting date; Job type (full-time, part-time, consultant); Job number

Resume database available: No

Employer profiles available: No

Costs for jobseekers to view jobs/ post a resume: Free; N/A

Costs for employers to list job openings/ view resumes: $40 for a 30-day listing. Jobs may only be listed by nonprofits. Resumes are not available.

Other key features: Nonprofit library and career resource center, which includes links to newsgroups, other online employment sites, and links to additional nonprofit sites.

Insider tips: National Opportunity NOCs ("Nonprofit Organization Classifieds") is brought to you by the same people who bring you *Opportunity NOCs*, the printed newsletter. The newsletter, with editions for Boston, New York, Philadelphia, and other metropolitan areas, details more than 1,100 new job listings each month to a subscriber base of more than 50,000. If you're a jobseeker looking for a new job in the nonprofit arena, or you're a nonprofit looking for employees, this is a good place to start.

NATIONJOB NETWORK

http://www.nationjob.com

Number of job listings: N/A

Types of jobs: All

Locations of jobs: United States and some international

Frequency of updates: Daily

Search criteria available: Company name; Job category; Keyword; Location; Salary; Skills; Job type (full-time, part-time, temporary, seasonal)

Resume database available: No

Employer profiles available: Yes

Costs for jobseekers to view jobs/ post a resume: Free; N/A

Costs for employers to list job openings/ view resumes: $95/two page listing for 30 days; $125/one page listing and a one page company profile for 30 days. Other pricing plans available.

Other key features: Extensive jobs database; a **job search agent** called P.J. Scout (serving 325,000 jobseekers per week at the time of this writing); a variety of specialty Web pages; and links to Websites of many sponsoring companies (all of whom have current job openings posted).

Insider tips: Presented by NationJob, Inc., this site also lists its openings on America's Job Bank, Alta Vista Careers, and Yahoo! Classifieds. Also, specialty pages enable job seekers to research companies in a particular employment category or geographical area. The "Community Pages" section offers current, local job information for much of the U.S.

NET-TEMPS

http://www.net-temps.com

Number of job listings: 70,000

Types of jobs: Mainly contract or temporary jobs; some full-time.
Administration; Business; Engineering; Finance; Health care; HR; IT.

Locations of jobs: United States and Canada

Frequency of updates: Daily

Search criteria available: Job category; Job type (contract or full-time);
Keyword; Location

Resume database available: Yes

Employer profiles available: Yes

Costs for jobseekers to view jobs/ post a resume: Free

Costs for employers to list job openings/ view resumes: A free 30-day
trial was being offered at the time of this writing. Fees are accessed after the
30-day trial.

Other key features: A chat room for jobseekers and recruiters
(limited operating times), and staffing agency profiles.

Insider tips: A good site with comprehensive job listings for those seeking
exposure to recruiters' openings in a variety of fields. This site lists thousands
of job listings from as many as 1,500 employment agencies. Placements are
contract, temporary, and permanent.

PASSPORTACCESS

http://www.passportaccess.com

Number of job listings: N/A

Types of jobs: Technical

Locations of jobs: United States

Frequency of updates: Daily

Search criteria available: Company name; Keyword; Location; Area code.

Resume database available: Yes

Employer profiles available: Yes

Costs for jobseekers to view jobs/ post a resume: Free

Costs for employers to list job openings/ view resumes: $700 for six months of unlimited job postings; $895/ year for unlimited access to resumes.

Other key features: An extensive database of job listings, and a special section (organized by company) with new positions posted daily. **Note:** Check the "Date of Last Posting" in the company section to make sure the listing is current. At the time of this writing, those dates ranged from a few days to several months.

Insider tips: Focusing on technical candidates and recruiters, PassportAccess enables you to see a company's entire list of available postings, go to the company's Website, or see what the position's requirements are before visiting it. Also, be sure to check out the Career Services page, which features direct links to computer magazines (*Computerworld, Wired*), salary and relocation services, career and resume services, electronic resume information, and much, much more.

PHILLIPS CAREER CENTER

http://www.phillips.com/careercenter.htm
Number of job listings: N/A
Types of jobs: All
Locations of jobs: United States
Frequency of updates: Daily
Search criteria available: Job category; Keyword; Location; Salary; Job type (full-time, part-time, contract, temporary)
Resume database available: No
Employer profiles available: No
Other key features: A **personal search agent** for jobseekers, notifying them of new listings matching their specified criteria.

RECRUITING-LINKS.COM

http://www.recruiting-links.com
Number of job listings: N/A
Types of jobs: All
Locations of jobs: United States, Canada, and Mexico
Frequency of updates: N/A
Search criteria available: Company name (sponsors); Industry; Job title; Location
Resume database available: No
Employer profiles available: Yes
Costs for jobseekers to view jobs/ post a resume: Free; N/A

Costs for employers to list job openings/ view resumes: A free 30-day trial was being offered at the time of this writing. Fees are accessed after the 30-day trial.

Other key features: Links to company Websites with job postings for a variety of top companies in various industries; offers company email addresses so that you may send your resume directly; and includes additional career site links.

Insider tips: The site is run by SkillSearch Corporation.

USA JOBS

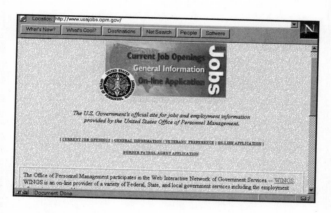

http://www.usajobs.opm.gov/

Number of job listings: N/A

Types of jobs: All

Locations of jobs: United States

Frequency of updates: Daily

Search criteria available: Job category; Job title; Keyword; Location; Agency; Posting date; Job series (GS level)

Resume database available: No

Employer profiles available: No

Costs for jobseekers to view jobs/ post a resume: Free; N/A

Costs for employers to list job openings/ view resumes: Jobs listed from government agencies only.

Other key features: Online career transition assistance provided by the United States Department of Labor, and various government information sources.

Insider tips: Operated by the United States Office of Personnel Management, USA Jobs is the U.S. government's official site for jobs and employment information. It contains information on: applying for federal jobs, federal salary and benefits, student employment, and more. Job listings are neatly divided into: professional; clerical and technical; trades and labor; senior executive; entry-level; worker-trainee; and summer positions. You can also conduct an alphabetical search of available jobs, search for a specific GS level, or search the government's Y2K openings.

WESTECH VIRTUAL JOB FAIR

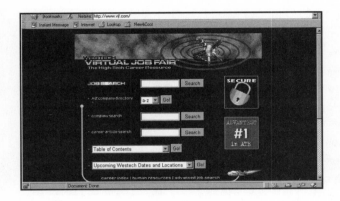

http://www.vjf.com
Number of job listings: 30,000
Types of jobs: All, with a focus on high-tech
Locations of jobs: United States and some international
Frequency of updates: Daily
Search criteria available: Company name; Keyword; Location
Resume database available: Yes (more than 160,000)
Employer profiles available: Yes
Costs for jobseekers to view jobs/ post a resume: Free
Costs for employers to list job openings/ view resumes: $300/month for 1-40 positions, $25/each additional position. There is a fee to access resumes.
Other key features: Schedule of job fairs; tons of career resources, including links to hi-tech magazines, a salary calculator, and more.

Insider tips: A good resource for those interested in high-tech fields. This site lists more than 30,000 jobs, hosts more than 160,000 resumes, and displays the dates for nearly 100 technical career fairs.

GEOGRAPHICALLY-SPECIFIC SITES

NORTHEAST/MID-ATLANTIC SITES

AMERICA'S TV JOB NETWORK

http://www.tvjobnet.com
Number of job listings: N/A
Types of jobs: Computer/Technical; Engineering; Financial/Insurance; Health care; Hospitality/Restaurant; Professional; Skilled labor/Manufacturing; Sales; Clerical; Management; Retail; General; Employment Services
Locations of jobs: United States (primarily PA, DE, and NJ)
Frequency of updates: N/A
Search criteria available: Job category; Location
Resume database available: Yes
Employer profiles available: Yes
Costs for jobseekers to view jobs/ post a resume: There is no charge to view jobs. There is a fee to post a resume. Please visit the site for more details.
Costs for employers to list job openings/ view resumes: Posting one listing will cost $25/month. Posting between two and five listings will cost $20 per month, per listing.
Other key features: Career training and other resources, including a salary calculator.
Insider tips: Information from this site is also part of a weekly television show in the Delaware Valley.

BOSTON.COM

http://www.boston.com
Number of job listings: 15,000

Types of jobs: All

Locations of jobs: Boston, Massachusetts metro area

Frequency of updates: Daily

Search criteria available: Job category; Keyword

Resume database available: Yes

Employer profiles available: Yes

Costs for jobseekers to view jobs/ post a resume: Free

Costs for employers to list job openings/ view resumes: $119/listing for four weeks. Resumes can be accessed through a link with CareerPath.com (password required).

Other key features: Access to career articles; a schedule of career fairs/ activities; a directory of Boston-area employment agencies and recruiters; and links to other career sites.

Insider tips: This site is a service of *The Boston Globe*, and includes both print and online-only listings.

BOSTON JOB BANK

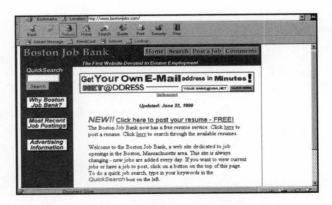

http://www.bostonjobs.com

Number of job listings: N/A

Types of jobs: All

Locations of jobs: Boston, Massachusetts metro area

Frequency of updates: Daily

Search criteria available: Job category; Keyword

Resume database available: Yes

Employer profiles available: No

Costs for jobseekers to view jobs/ post a resume: Free

Costs for employers to list job openings/ view resumes: $20/ad for four weeks. There is no charge to search resumes.

Other key features: Separate search functions allow you to search most recent job and resume postings.

Insider tips: A simple, no frills career site. Though there are a limited number of job and resume postings (compared with sites such as Monster.com), the site does provide current, thorough information.

BOSTONSEARCH

http://www.bostonsearch.com

Number of job listings: More than 1,000

Types of jobs: All, but with an emphasis on technical and computer-related listings

Locations of jobs: Boston, Massachusetts metro area

Frequency of updates: Daily

Search criteria available: Job category; Keyword; Type of position (regular permanent, contract, etc.)

Resume database available: Yes

Employer profiles available: Yes

Costs for jobseekers to view jobs/ post a resume: Free

Costs for employers to list job openings/ view resumes: Job listings and profiles can be listed by employers for 45 days, ranging in cost from $70 to $6,000.

Other key features: Weekly career advice column.

Insider tips: This site is host to several Boston metro area businesses, including those with job listings, and those with profiles and job listings.

CLASSIFIND NETWORK

http://www.classifind.com

Number of job listings: N/A

Types of jobs: All

Locations of jobs: Northeast and Mid-Atlantic states

Frequency of updates: N/A

Search criteria available: Job category; Job title; Location; Salary; Job type (full-time, part-time)

Resume database available: No

Employer profiles available: No

Costs for jobseekers to view jobs/ post a resume: Free; N/A

Costs for employers to list job openings/ view resumes: N/A; resumes are not available.

Other key features: N/A

JOBNET

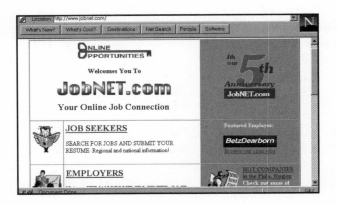

http://www.jobnet.com

Number of job listings: 1,000

Types of jobs: All

Locations of jobs: Most jobs are in PA, NJ, and DE (Philadelphia metro area)

Frequency of updates: Daily

Search criteria available: Keyword; Company name; or view all jobs

Resume database available: Yes

Employer profiles available: Yes

Costs for jobseekers to view jobs/ post a resume: Free

Costs for employers to list job openings/ view resumes: $75 to list one ad on JobNet; $495 to list one ad on JobNet and its five online partners (4Work, CareerMagazine, CareerSite, CareerWeb, and NationJob); $1,150 for one ad at these sites plus JobOptions, CareerMosaic, Monster.com, and a tenth site of your choice. You can also list an ad at any one of these sites through JobNet (rates vary). Employers do pay a fee to search resumes.

Other key features: "Online Opportunities" newsletter, and information on regional job fairs.

Insider tips: This small, localized database is noteworthy for its partnerships with Web giants like CareerWeb and CareerMagazine. As a subscriber to JobNet, you can post to JobNet's Philadelphia-area database for free. Jobseekers can also link to specific companies listed at the site, view their job openings, and submit a resume for free.

NEW ENGLAND OPPORTUNITY NOCS

http://www.opnocs.org
Number of job listings: N/A
Types of jobs: Nonprofit
Locations of jobs: New England
Frequency of updates: N/A
Search criteria available: Job title
Resume database available: No
Employer profiles available: No
Costs for jobseekers to view jobs/ post a resume: Free; N/A
Costs for employers to list job openings/ view resumes: $50/45-word ad/per issue. Additional pricing plans available. Resumes are not available.
Other key features: Internships and volunteer listings; and links to other non-profit sites, including the National Opportunity NOCs site.
Insider tips: This site offers some of the New England listings from the Opportunity NOCs (Nonprofit Organization Classifieds) biweekly print newsletter. The listings at this site do not represent all of the listings found in the newsletter, and are displayed about one week after the newsletter is sent to subscribers.

NEW JERSEY ONLINE

http://www.nj.com
Number of job listings: 1,100
Types of jobs: All
Locations of jobs: New Jersey
Frequency of updates: Nearly every hour
Search criteria available: Job category; Keyword; Newspaper (NJ newspaper classifieds are in the database)
Resume database available: No
Employer profiles available: No

Costs for jobseekers to view jobs/ post a resume: Free; N/A

Costs for employers to list job openings/ view resumes: Please contact the site for pricing information. Resumes are not available.

Other key features: Forums and news; information on employment agencies and technical schools; and career advice.

Insider tips: This site gets roughly two million visits per month.

PHILADELPHIA ONLINE

http://www.phillynews.com

Number of job listings: N/A

Types of jobs: All

Locations of jobs: Mostly Pennsylvania

Frequency of updates: Daily

Search criteria available: Job category; Keyword; Posting date

Resume database available: No

Employer profiles available: Yes

Costs for jobseekers to view jobs/ post a resume: Free; N/A

Costs for employers to list job openings/ view resumes: $48.60 for three lines, for seven days. Resumes are not available.

Other key features: Links to employment agencies, computer training services, and resume services.

Insider tips: Detailed employer profiles cover such topics as working environment and hot jobs at the company. This site is associated with CareerPath.com.

TOWNONLINE.COM/WORKING

http://www.townonline.com/working

Number of jobs listings: 100

Types of jobs: All

Locations of jobs: New England (primarily Eastern Massachusetts)

Frequency of updates: N/A

Search criteria available: Job category; Location; Keyword; Ad number

Resume database available: No

Employer profiles available: Yes

Costs for jobseekers to view jobs/ post a resume: Free; N/A

Costs for employers to list job openings/ view resumes: $28/ad and up. Registration is required. Resumes are not available.

Other key features: Local news and information; a question and answer career forum; links to online career resources; and resources for human resource professionals and recruiters, including related news articles, a free newsletter, and more. **Insider tips:** Whether you are looking for a job or you're looking to fill a job in Eastern Massachusetts, you'll benefit by stopping by this site. While the number of job listings is relatively limited, there are many other services here you'll find useful.

VERMONT DEPARTMENT OF EMPLOYMENT AND TRAINING

http://www.det.state.vt.us

Number of job listings: N/A

Types of jobs: All

Locations of jobs: Vermont (also has access to nationwide listings)

Frequency of updates: Daily

Search criteria available: Job category; Keyword; Location; Skills; Job type (full-time, part-time)

Resume database available: Yes

Employer profiles available: No

Costs for jobseekers to view jobs/ post a resume: Free

Costs for employers to list job openings/ view resumes: Free to Vermont employers.

Other key features: "Labor Market Information" section offers access to Vermont labor market information, unemployment rates, statewide wages, and employment statistics; a summer jobs section; access to Federal and national job listings; and links to additional job listings and training programs.

Insider tips: Jobseekers registered with this site may request that a referral be sent from the Vermont Department of Employment and Training directly to an employer.

VIRGINIA EMPLOYMENT COMMISSION

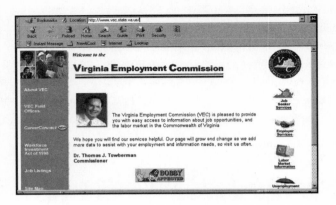

http://www.vec.state.va.us
Number of job listings: N/A
Types of jobs: All
Locations of jobs: Primarily Virginia
Frequency of updates: N/A
Search criteria available: Job category; Location; Salary; Skills; Posting date; Experience level
Resume database available: Yes
Employer profiles available: No
Costs for jobseekers to view jobs/ post a resume: Free
Costs for employers to list job openings/ view resumes: Free
Other key features: Information on occupational trends, wages, and geographic areas, and links to more career resources.
Insider tips: Some services at this site require registration, but all are free.

WORKFORCE NEW JERSEY PUBLIC INFORMATION NETWORK

http://nj.jobsearch.org
Number of job listings: N/A
Types of jobs: All
Locations of jobs: Primarily New Jersey (also has some national listings)
Frequency of updates: N/A

Search criteria available: Job category; Location; Salary; Skills; Posting date; Experience level

Resume database available: Yes

Employer profiles available: No

Costs for jobseekers to view jobs/ post a resume: Free

Costs for employers to list job openings/ view resumes: Free

Other key features: Information on occupational trends, wages, and geographic areas; and a "Career and Resource Library."

Insider tips: Some of the services on this site require registration, but all are free.

SOUTHEAST SITES

CAREERGUIDE

http://www.careerguide.com

Number of job listings: 1,400

Types of jobs: All

Locations of jobs: Southeastern United States (with an emphasis on Atlanta, GA)

Frequency of updates: N/A (listings are removed after 30 days)

Search criteria available: Company name; Job category; Keyword; Location

Resume database available: Yes

Employer profiles available: Yes

Costs for jobseekers to view jobs/ post a resume: Free

Costs for employers to list job openings/ view resumes: To post a job listing, submit the online form and submit to CareerGuide - a representative will contact you regarding payment. Resume access is password protected.

Other key features: "ResuNet" is a resume service for recruiters, listing the most appropriate resumes from its database that match a recruiters criteria. CareerGuide will then email the list of applicants directly to the recruiter; **"e-Signal" is an email service for jobseekers**, notifying them of new listings matching their criteria; and "The Bridge" online newsletter serves both jobseekers and employers.

Insider tips: This site has a number of services for both the jobseeker and the recruiter.

CAROLINASCAREERWEB

http://www.carolinascareerweb.com

Number of job listings: N/A

Types of jobs: All

Locations of jobs: North Carolina and South Carolina

Frequency of updates: N/A

Search criteria available: Job category; Keyword; Location

Resume database available: Yes

Employer profiles available: Yes

Costs for jobseekers to view jobs/ post a resume: Free

Costs for employers to list job openings/ view resumes: Different membership plans, including job listings and resume access, are offered. Please visit the site for more information.

Other key features: Resume storage; regional information; and an "Account Manager" for employers, which allows them to modify listings and check on statistics and responses related to their ads.

Insider tips: If you're interested in working in the Carolinas, this is a site you've got to visit. If you opt to file your resume at this site, you can choose to either save it, or save it and allow employers to view it. By simply saving your resume, you can search for jobs on CarolinasCareerWeb, and when you find one you'd like to apply for, you've got your resume right at the site, and it's a few clicks away from being submitted.

FLORIDA CAREER LINK

http://www.floridacareerlink.com

Number of job listings: N/A

Types of jobs: All

Locations of jobs: Florida

Frequency of updates: Weekly

Search criteria available: Company name; Job category; Keyword; Location; Job type (full-time, part-time)

Resume database available: No

Employer profiles available: Yes

Costs for jobseekers to view jobs/ post a resume: Free; N/A

Costs for employers to list job openings/ view resumes: Please contact the site for pricing information. Resumes are not available.

Other key features: Information on local career fairs; relocation information; and links to recruiters and other career sites.

Insider tips: Job listings are current and fairly well detailed.

TRIANGLE JOBS.COM

http://www.trianglejobs.com
Number of job listings: N/A
Types of jobs: All
Locations of jobs: North and South Carolina
Frequency of updates: N/A
Search criteria available: Job category; Job title; Posting date
Resume database available: Yes
Employer profiles available: Yes
Costs for jobseekers to view jobs/ post a resume: Free
Costs for employers to list job openings/ view resumes: Prices start at $14 per line. There is a fee to access the resume database. Please contact the site for more information.
Other key features: Job training and job fairs information; a career advice column; and tips on job search topics such as writing a resume and negotiating an offer.
Insider tips: If you're interested in getting tips and different perspectives on the job search, in addition to helpful services like jobs and resume databases and relocation information, then you'll want to stop by TriangleJobs.com.

MIDWEST SITES

CAREERBOARD

http://www.careerboard.com
Types of jobs: All
Locations of jobs: Greater Cleveland and Akron, Ohio area
Search criteria available: Company name; Industry; Job category; Keyword
Resume database available: Yes
Employer profiles available: Yes
Costs for jobseekers to view jobs/ post a resume: Free
Costs for employers to list job openings/ view resumes: $97/posting for 30 days. Resume access costs $350/month for two users with a three month contract, or $3,500/year for two users, which also includes unlimited job postings.

CAREERLINK

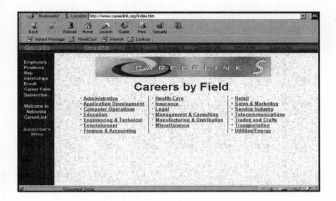

http://www.careerlink.org/index.htm
Number of job listings: N/A
Types of jobs: All
Locations of jobs: Nebraska
Frequency of updates: N/A
Search criteria available: Job category; Job title
Resume database available: Yes
Employer profiles available: Yes
Costs for jobseekers to view jobs/ post a resume: Free
Costs for employers to list job openings/ view resumes: $125 per job listing. Pricing plans are available, ranging from $600 to $3,000. Resumes may be searched for a fee - please contact CareerLink for more details.
Other key features: Detailed employer profiles and job descriptions.
Insider tips: This is an impressive site, and one of the few sites you will find devoted to employment in Nebraska. The site claims to list more than 1,700 jobs from nearly 140 Nebraska employers, and hosts roughly 5,600 resumes.

CHICAGO SOFTWARE NEWS

http://www.chisoft.com
Number of job listings: 580
Types of jobs: Computer/ IT
Locations of jobs: Illinois (emphasis is on Chicago)
Frequency of updates: Daily

Search criteria available: Keyword
Resume database available: No
Employer profiles available: Yes

KANSAS JOB-BANK

http://entkdhr.ink.org/kjb/index.html
Number of job listings: N/A
Types of jobs: All
Locations of jobs: Kansas (with additional listings for Missouri, and some nationwide listings)
Frequency of updates: N/A
Search criteria available: Job category; Keyword; Location
Resume database available: Yes
Employer profiles available: Yes
Costs for jobseekers to view jobs/ post a resume: Free
Costs for employers to list job openings/ view resumes: Free
Other key features: "Job Match" email service notifies jobseekers of new listings that match their criteria.
Insider tips: A resourceful site with solid search and resume capabilities.

MINNESOTA JOBS.COM

http://www.minnesotajobs.com
Types of jobs: All
Locations of jobs: Minnesota
Search criteria available: Job category; Keyword
Resume database available: No
Employer profiles available: Yes

ONLINE COLUMBIA

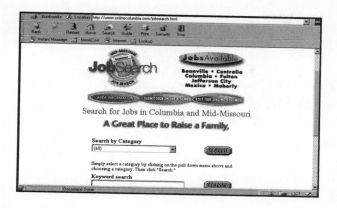

http://www.onlinecolumbia.com
Types of jobs: All
Locations of jobs: Missouri
Search criteria available: Job category; Keyword
Resume database available: No
Employer profiles available: No

STL DIRECT

http://directory.st-louis.mo.us/
Number of job listings: N/A
Types of jobs: All
Locations of jobs: St. Louis, Missouri area
Frequency of updates: N/A
Search criteria available: N/A
Resume database available: N/A
Employer profiles available: N/A
Costs for jobseekers to view jobs/ post a resume: N/A
Costs for employers to list job openings/ view resumes: N/A
Other key features: Newsgroup links; local information; and links to area recruiters and businesses.
Insider tips: This site does not offer job listings or a resume database. What it does offer are career-related links for the St. Louis area, including homepages of local recruiters and local newsgroups. To find jobs on this site, type in "jobs"

in the "Show Me" search box at the top of STL Direct's homepage. Next you will see a screen with "Job Placement" as one of your options. Click on "Job Placement." From there you will be introduced to a variety of local links.

WISCONSIN JOBNET

http://www.dwd.state.wi.us/jobnet
Types of jobs: All
Locations of jobs: Wisconsin; Iowa; Minnesota; Northern Illinois; Michigan Upper Peninsula
Search criteria available: Company name; Job title; Keyword; Location
Resume database available: No
Employer profiles available: No
Costs for jobseekers to view jobs/ post a resume: Free; N/A
Costs for employers to list job openings/ view resumes: Free; N/A
Insider tips: This site also provides access to national job listings.

WEST / SOUTHWEST SITES

ALASKA JOBS CENTER

http://www.ilovealaska.com/alaskajobs
Types of jobs: Computers; Construction/Engineering/Design
Locations of jobs: Alaska
Resume database available: No (there is a jobs wanted section)
Employer profiles available: No
Other key features: Lots of links to related sites.

THE CALIFORNIA JOB SOURCE

http://www.statejobs.com/ca.html
Number of job listings: N/A
Types of jobs: All
Locations of jobs: California
Frequency of updates: N/A

Search criteria available: Keyword; Location
Resume database available: No
Employer profiles available: Yes

COLORADOJOBS.COM

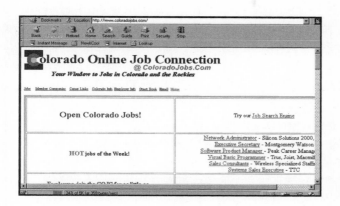

http://www.coloradojobs.com
Number of job listings: N/A
Types of jobs: Administration/Clerical; Computers;
Construction/Engineering/Design; Finance/Economics; Sales
Locations of jobs: Colorado
Frequency of updates: N/A
Search criteria available: Company name; Industry; Job title; Keyword;
Location
Resume database available: No
Employer profiles available: No

GOVERNMENT LISTING OF
BAY AREA EMPLOYMENT

http://www.abag.ca.gov/bayarea/commerce/globe/globe.html
Number of job listings: N/A
Types of jobs: Government, including: Administration/Clerical;
Education/Library Sciences; Finance/Economics; Health Care; Legal;
Managerial; Executive/Consulting; Scientific
Locations of jobs: California

Frequency of updates: N/A

Search criteria available: Job title; Location

Resume database available: No

Employer profiles available: No

Costs for jobseekers to view jobs/ post a resume: Free; N/A

Costs for employers to list job openings/ view resumes: Free; N/A

Other key features: This site also has a link that lists local government job lists by city for California. The address is **http://www.abag.ca.gov/bayarea/ commerce/globe/other_loc.html**.

HOUSTONCHRONICLE.COM

http://www.chron.com

Number of job listings: N/A

Types of jobs: All

Locations of jobs: Texas (Houston area)

Frequency of updates: Daily

Search criteria available: Job category; Job title; Keyword; Posting date

Resume database available: No

Employer profiles available: No

Costs for jobseekers to view jobs/ post a resume: Free; N/A

Costs for employers to list job openings/ view resumes: Employers should contact the *Houston Chronicle* for pricing information. Resumes are not available.

Other key features: Local news and community forums.

Insider tips: This site is the online version of the *Houston Chronicle* newspaper.

ORANGE COUNTY REGISTER

http://www.ocregister.com/ads/classified/index.shtml

Number of job listings: 800

Types of jobs: All

Locations of jobs: Orange County, California

Frequency of updates: Daily

Search criteria available: Job category; Keyword; Posting date

Resume database available: No

Employer profiles available: No

Costs for jobseekers to view jobs/ post a resume: Free; N/A

Costs for employers to list job openings/ view resumes: There is a fee to list a job opening. Employers may submit their ad online, and a representative will contact them with the price of the ad. Resumes are not available.

Insider tips: This site is the online version of the *Orange County Register*, a print newspaper read by more than one million people.

THE SILICON VALLEY JOB SOURCE

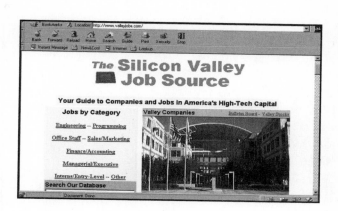

http://www.valleyjobs.com

Number of job listings: N/A

Types of jobs: All

Locations of jobs: California: San Francisco, Oakland, Fremont, Palo Alto, San Mateo, San Jose, Santa Clara, and Sunnyvale (can also search other states)

Frequency of updates: N/A

Search criteria available: Company name; Keyword; Location

Resume database available: Yes

Employer profiles available: Yes

Costs for jobseekers to view jobs/ post a resume: Free; $10 to post a resume for 90 days.

Costs for employers to list job openings/ view resumes: Free (postings only from Bay area companies - no search firms). No charge to view resumes.

Other key features: Regional information; company links broken down by different areas of Silicon Valley; a government jobs section; links to venture capital firms; and links to news sources in the Bay area, both print and online.

Insider tips: Are you looking for a job with some of the best high-tech companies in the country? If so, check out this site, which has direct links to companies like Apple Computer, Yahoo!, Intel, and Oracle. This site also links to companies like Levi Strauss, Visa, as well as local and state government sites, and more.

680CAREERS.COM

http://www.680careers.com
Number of job listings: N/A
Types of jobs: N/A
Locations of jobs: California (Contra Costa and Alameda Counties)
Frequency of updates: Monthly
Search criteria available: N/A
Resume database available: No
Employer profiles available: Yes
Costs for jobseekers to view jobs/ post a resume: Free
Costs for employers to list job openings/ view resumes: Free (certain restrictions apply)
Other key features: "Resubot" email service – jobseekers may select from a list of companies at the site, and email a cover letter and resume to those companies; local information and resources; and news of upcoming career fairs.
Insider tips: This is not a job posting site. Jobseekers may look here to find links to major corporations in the 680 corridor of the above mentioned counties in California. Many of the companies we found at this site were either high-tech/computer or communications related.

TOPJOBS USA

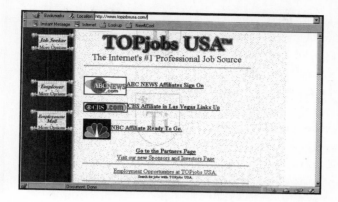

http://www.topjobsusa.com

Number of job listings: 50,000

Types of jobs: All, including professional, managerial, and technical positions

Locations of jobs: Emphasis is on Western United States—Arizona, California, Colorado, Idaho, Nevada, New Mexico, Oregon, Texas, Utah, and Washington—but nationwide job listings are also provided

Frequency of updates: Weekly

Search criteria available: Location; Job title; Company name; Posting date; Full text

Resume database available: Yes

Employer profiles available: Yes

Costs for jobseekers to view jobs/ post a resume: Free

Costs for employers to list job openings/ view resumes: $125/ job listing for eight weeks. Other pricing plans are available. Prices for viewing resumes were not available at the time of this writing.

Other key features: Links to other career resources, including classifieds and general job listing sites.

Insider tips: While its focus remains on the Western United States, TOPjobs USA contains thousands of job listings for the Midwest and the East. Check out Career Central, offering career, resume, and interviewing tips.

WASHINGTON EMPLOYMENT WEB PAGES

http://members.aol.com/gwattier/washjob.htm
Number of job listings: N/A
Types of jobs: N/A
Locations of jobs: Washington state
Frequency of updates: N/A
Search criteria available: N/A
Resume database available: No
Employer profiles available: Yes
Costs for jobseekers to view jobs/ post a resume: N/A
Costs for employers to lists job openings/ view resumes: N/A
Other key features: Links to public and private employer Websites; links to other Washington employment sites; and general Washington state information.
Insider tips: You will not find actual job listings at this site, but you will find links to more than 1,300 employment sites. A good starting point for people interested in working in Washington state.

INTERNATIONAL SITES

ASIA NET

http://www.asia-net.com
Types of jobs: All (focus is on bilingual jobs)
Locations of jobs: International
Search criteria available: Job category; Keyword
Resume database available: No
Employer profiles available: No
Insider tips: Languages involved are Japanese, Chinese, Korean, and English.

AUSTRALIAN JOB SEARCH

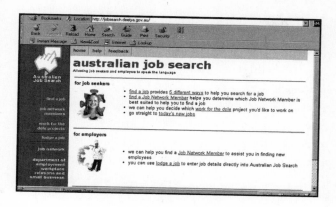

http://jobsearch.deetya.gov.au
Types of jobs: All
Locations of jobs: International (Australia)
Search criteria available: Industry; Job category; Location; Seasonal employment
Resume database available: No
Employer profiles available: No
Insider tips: This site is a service of the Australian Government.

BYRON EMPLOYMENT AUSTRALIA

http://employment.byron.com.au
Types of jobs: All
Locations of jobs: International (Australia)
Search criteria available: Job category
Resume database available: No
Employer profiles available: No
Costs for jobseekers to view jobs/ post a resume: Free; N/A
Costs for employers to list job openings/ view resumes: $30 for four weeks, and the price decreases as you increase the number of postings per month. Resumes are not available.

CANADIAN JOBS CATALOGUE

http://www.kenevacorp.mb.ca

Types of jobs: All

Locations of jobs: International (Canada)

Search criteria available: Keyword

Resume database available: Yes

Employer profiles available: No

Costs for jobseeker to view jobs/ post a resume: $10 annual membership fee. There is a $10 fee for posting a resume for six months.

Costs for employers to list job openings/ view resumes: Rates vary for job postings. Please contact the site for more information. Resumes may be accessed free of charge.

CAREER INDIA

http://www.careerindia.com

Types of jobs: Computers; Construction/Engineering/Design

Locations of jobs: International (India)

Frequency of updates: Daily

Search criteria available: Job title

Resume database available: Yes

Employer profiles available: No

THE CHEMISTRY JOB HUNTERS GUIDE

http://www.cpes.sussex.ac.uk/resgrps/sjc/jobhunt.html
Number of job listings: None
Types of jobs: Chemistry/Science
Locations of jobs: International
Insider tips: This is not a jobs or resume site. It is a very small site, yet it provides some helpful links to International scientific companies, and some direct links to company career pages. Links to related career sites and search engines are also offered.

HUMAN RESOURCES ON-LINE

http://www.hro.ru/ru/db/partners/37.htm
Types of jobs: All
Locations of jobs: International (primarily Russia, but there are other international listings, and some from the United States)
Search criteria available: Job category; Job title; Location
Resume database available: Yes
Employer profiles available: No

INDOSCAPE

http://www.indoscape.com
Types of jobs: All
Locations of jobs: International (Indonesia)
Search criteria available: Company name; Job category; Job ID number; Posting date
Resume database available: Yes
Employer profiles available: Yes

THE IRISH JOBS PAGE

http://www.exp.ie
Types of jobs: All
Locations of jobs: International (mostly Ireland, but there are some other international listings)

Search criteria available: Company name; Job category; Keyword; Top companies/agencies

Resume database available: Yes

Employer profiles available: No

JOBSERVE

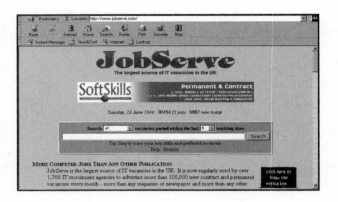

http://www.jobserve.com

Number of job listings: 30,000

Types of jobs: Information Technology; Computers; Managerial/Executive/Consulting

Locations of jobs: The United Kingdom and throughout Europe (more than 10 percent of the listings are reportedly international)

Frequency of updates: Daily

Search criteria available: Keyword (which can include location); Job type (contract, permanent, or both); Posting date

Resume database available: Yes

Employer profiles available: Yes

Costs for jobseekers to view jobs/ post a resume: Free

Costs for employers to list job openings/ view resumes: N/A

Other key features: Links to company Web pages, many of which are IT recruitment specialists; inclusion of your resume on a list sent to more than 1,000 IT recruitment specialists across the UK and Europe; several different options to **have job listings emailed to you** (more than 85,000 subscribers at the time of this writing); and a directory of recruiters including contact information and email addresses.

Insider tips: This site helps to put the World into WWW. Focusing on Information Technology jobs overseas, JobServe has an impressive array of clever benefits for job seekers. "Instants" is a page on the site that features the newest job listings each day, and is automatically updated each time a position is posted online. Reload often!

JOBSITE GROUP

http://www.jobsite.co.uk
Types of jobs: All
Locations of jobs: International (Europe)
Search criteria available: Company name; Job category; Job title; Keyword
Resume database available: No
Employer profiles available: Yes

JOBSTREET

http://www.jobstreet.com
Types of jobs: All
Locations of jobs: International (Malaysia)
Search criteria available: Company name; Industry; Job title; Keyword; Location; Posting date
Resume database available: No
Employer profiles available: Yes

OVERSEAS JOBS EXPRESS

http://www.overseasjobs.com
Types of jobs: All
Locations of jobs: United Kingdom and other international locations
Search criteria available: Job category

WORKWEB

http://www.workweb.co.uk
Types of jobs: All

Locations of jobs: International (United Kingdom)
Search criteria available: Job category; Keyword; Location
Resume database available: No
Employer profiles available: No

VACANCIES

http://www.vacancies.ac.uk
Number of job listings: N/A
Types of jobs: Mostly in higher-education
Locations of jobs: United Kingdom
Frequency of updates: N/A
Search criteria available: Job category; Keyword; Posting date; Job type (temporary, contract, research)
Resume database available: No
Employer profiles available: No
Costs for jobseekers to view jobs/ post a resume: Free; N/A
Costs for employers to list job openings/ view resumes: Free; N/A
Other key features: Links to related online resources.
Insider tips: This site is operated by National Information Services and Systems.

INDUSTRY-SPECIFIC SITES

ACCOUNTING/ BANKING/FINANCE

ACCOUNTING & FINANCE JOBS

http://www.accountingjobs.com
Number of jobs listed: N/A
Types of jobs: Accounting; Financial services
Locations of jobs: United States and some international
Frequency of updates: N/A

Search criteria available: Company name; Job category; Job title; Location
Resume database available: Yes
Employer profiles available: Yes
Costs for jobseekers to view jobs/ post a resume: Free
Costs for employers to list job openings/ view resumes: $160/listing for 30 days. There is no charge to view resumes.
Other key features: Links to other accounting and finance resources, such as AccountingStudents.com; and a research library.
Insider tips: This site is a service of CareerMosaic and AccountingNet.

ACCOUNTING.COM

http://www.accounting.com
Number of job listings: N/A
Types of jobs: Accounting
Locations of jobs: United States
Frequency of updates: At least every three weeks
Search criteria available: Job category; Keyword
Resume database available: Yes
Employer profiles available: No
Costs for jobseekers to view jobs/ post a resume: Free
Costs for employers to list job openings/ view resumes: $45/listing for one month. Resumes can be searched for $175, a price which also includes five job postings.
Other key features: Visitors can take part on a few discussion groups, and also get helpful tips on writing a resume.
Insider tips: We found a variety of fields covered by doing a general job search, with positions in accounting, Web design, and other technical positions.

ACCOUNTING NET

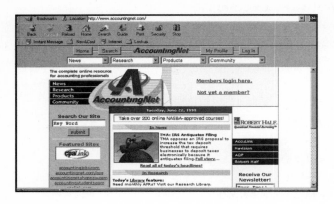

http://www.accountingnet.com

Number of job listings: N/A

Types of jobs: Accounting

Locations of jobs: United States and some international

Frequency of updates: N/A

Search criteria available: Company name; Job title; Keyword; Location

Resume database available: Yes

Employer profiles available: Yes

Costs for jobseekers to view jobs/ post a resume: Free

Costs for employers to list job openings/ view resumes: $160/ad for 30 days. There is no charge to search resumes.

Other key features: Links to related news and career resources.

Insider tips: This site is a service of CareerMosaic, one of the largest job sites on the Web.

AMERICAN BANKER ONLINE'S CAREERZONE

http://www.americanbanker.com/careerzone

Number of job listings: N/A

Types of jobs: All (focus on Financial Services)

Locations of jobs: United States

Frequency of updates: Daily

Search criteria available: Job category; Job type (full-time, part-time, contract, temporary); Keyword; Location; Salary
Resume database available: No
Employer profiles available: No

BLOOMBERG.COM

http://www.bloomberg.com
Number of job listings: N/A
Types of jobs: Financial Services
Locations of jobs: United States and some international
Frequency of updates: N/A
Search criteria available: Job category; Job title; Location
Resume database available: No
Employer profiles available: No

CFO'S FEATURED JOBS

http://www.cfonet.com/html/cfojobs.html
Number of job listings: N/A
Types of jobs: Chief Financial Officer; Treasurer; Senior Financial Executive
Locations of jobs: United States
Frequency of updates: N/A
Search criteria available: Job category; Location
Resume database available: No
Employer profiles available: No

FINANCIAL, ACCOUNTING, AND INSURANCE JOBS PAGE

http://www.nationjob.com/financial
Number of job listings: N/A
Types of jobs: Accounting; Financial Services; Insurance
Locations of jobs: United States
Frequency of updates: N/A
Search criteria available: Job category; Job title; Keyword; Location; Salary

Resume database available: No

Employer profiles available: Yes

Costs for jobseekers to view jobs/ post a resume: Free; N/A

Costs for employers to list job openings/ view resumes: $95 for a two-page listing; $125 for a two-page listing with a one-page employer profile. Other pricing plans are available, ranging from $495 to $5,500.

Other key features: Links to top employers, including The Hartford and BlueCross BlueShield; and **"P.J. Scout" email service** notifies jobseekers of new opportunities.

Insider tips: This site is part of the NationJob Network, and offers the same services and payment options. However, this site focuses solely on financial-related employment.

FINCAREER.COM

http://www.fincareer.com

Number of job listings: N/A

Types of jobs: Financial Services

Locations of jobs: United States and some international

Frequency of updates: N/A

Search criteria available: Company name; Job title; Location

Resume database available: No

Employer profiles available: No

JOBS FOR BANKERS ONLINE

http://www.bankjobs.com

Number of job listings: 15,300

Types of jobs: Banking; Financial Services

Locations of jobs: United States

Frequency of updates: Job listings updated twice per week; resumes are added daily.

Search criteria available: Keyword; Location

Resume database available: Yes

Employer profiles available: No

Costs for jobseekers to view jobs/ post a resume: There is no charge to post a resume. In order to view jobs, a jobseeker must first submit a resume;

however, if they'd rather not post a resume, the jobs database can be accessed for $49 for six months.

Costs for employers to list job openings/ view resumes: There is no charge for posting a job. There is a charge for accessing resumes. Please contact the site for more details.

Other key features: Links to lots of other banking-related sites.

Insider tips: One of a limited number of sites that allow free access by jobseekers, *and* free job posting services to employers. A password is required for jobseekers to access the jobs database, but the password is free (resume posting required).

NATIONAL BANKING NETWORK

http://www.banking-financejobs.com
Number of job listings: N/A
Types of jobs: Banking/ Financial Services
Locations of jobs: United States
Frequency of updates: Weekly
Search criteria available: Job category; Job title; Location
Resume database available: Yes
Employer profiles available: No

ADVERTISING/ MARKETING/ PUBLIC RELATIONS

ADWEEK ONLINE

http://www.adweek.com
Number of job listings: 190
Types of jobs: Advertising/Marketing (Account Management/PR; Creative; Marketing/Brand Management; Media; Publishing; TV/Radio; Production; Miscellaneous; New Media/IT)
Locations of jobs: United States
Frequency of updates: Weekly
Search criteria available: Company name; Job category; Keyword; Location

Resume database available: No
Employer profiles available: No

DIRECT MARKETING WORLD

http://www.dmworld.com
Number of job postings: N/A
Types of jobs: Marketing
Locations of jobs: United States
Frequency of updates: N/A
Search criteria available: Job category; Location; Posting date
Resume database available: Yes
Employer profiles available: No
Costs for jobseekers to view jobs/ post a resume: Free
Costs for employers to list job openings/ view resumes: Free
Other key features: A "library" with news articles and newsletters, and a calendar or events in the direct marketing field.
Insider tips: This site also offers mailing lists and databases for direct marketing professionals.

MARKETING JOBS

http://www.marketingjobs.com
Number of job listings: N/A
Types of jobs: Advertising; Marketing; Sales
Locations of jobs: United States
Frequency of updates: N/A
Search criteria available: Job title; Keyword; Location; Salary
Resume database available: Yes
Employer profiles available: No

A E R O S P A C E

AVIATION AND AEROSPACE JOBS PAGE

http://www.nationjob.com/aviation

Number of job listings: N/A

Types of jobs: Aerospace/Aviation (includes: computers, construction/engineering/design, managerial/executive/consulting, sales, and more)

Locations of jobs: United States

Frequency of updates: N/A

Search criteria available: Job category; Job title

Resume database available: No

Employer profiles available: Yes

Costs for jobseekers to view jobs/ post a resume: Free; N/A

Costs for employers to list job openings/ view resumes: $95 for a two-page listing for 30 days, or $125 for a two-page listing and a one-page company profile. Other pricing plans are offered. Resumes are not available.

Other key features: Listings are cross-posted on other sites such as Yahoo! Classifieds and America's Job Bank; and this site uses NationJob's **"PJ Scout "** **email service**.

Insider tips: This site is part of the NationJob Network.

AVIATION EMPLOYMENT.COM

http://www.aviationemployment.com

Number of job listings: N/A

Types of jobs: Aviation/Airlines

Locations of jobs: United States

Frequency of updates: N/A

Search criteria available: Company name; Job category; Location; Salary; Skills; Job type (full-time, part-time, permanent, contract)

Resume database available: No

Employer profiles available: Yes

SPACE JOBS

http://www.spacejobs.com

Number of job listings: N/A

Types of jobs: Aerospace

Locations of jobs: United States and some international

Frequency of updates: N/A

Search criteria available: Company name; Keyword; Location

Resume database available: No

Employer profiles available: Yes

Costs for jobseekers to view jobs/ post a resume: Free; N/A

Costs for employers to list job openings/ view resumes: $225/listing (50% discount available to nonprofit and educational institutions). Resumes are not available.

Other key features: Email service notifying jobseekers of new opportunities; a schedule of related conferences; and a "What's New" section linking to the most recent job listings.

Insider tips: Check out the "List of All Organizations" for links to aerospace companies worldwide.

ARTS & ENTERTAINMENT

THE INTERNET MUSIC PAGES

http://www.musicpages.com

Types of jobs: Arts and Entertainment (Music)

Locations of jobs: United States and some international

Search criteria available: None

Insider tips: This site also provides links to music-related newsgroups. Job listings come from companies like Dolby, Microsoft, and Fender.

ONLINE SPORTS.COM

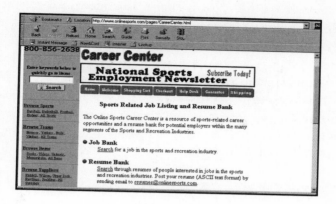

http://www.onlinesports.com/pages/CareerCenter.html
Number of job listings: N/A
Types of jobs: Sports and Recreation
Locations of jobs: United States
Frequency of updates: Bi-weekly
Search criteria available: N/A
Resume database available: No
Employer profiles available: Yes
Costs for jobseeker to view jobs/ post a resume: Free; N/A
Costs for employers to list job openings/ view resumes: Free; N/A
Insider tips: While most jobs were posted as "Open until filled," we found at least a few job postings that had expired. Make sure to check the closing date of any ad you may be interested in responding to.

B I O T E C H N O L O G Y / S C I E N T I F I C

BIO ONLINE

http://www.bio.com
Number of job listings: 470
Types of jobs: Life sciences

Locations of jobs: United States and China

Frequency of updates: N/A

Search criteria available: Company name; Job category; Keyword; Location

Resume database available: Yes

Employer database available: Yes

Costs for jobseekers to view jobs/ post a resume: Free

Costs for employers to list job openings/ view resumes: N/A

Other key features: Links to industry news and activities, and links to research and education sources.

Insider tips: This site had relatively few job listings, and most of the jobs were from a limited number of companies.

SCIENCE PROFESSIONAL NETWORK

http://www.recruitsciencemag.org

Number of job listings: 450

Types of jobs: Various scientific fields

Locations of jobs: United States and some international (including: Africa, Asia, Canada, Europe, Latin America, Middle East, and South Pacific)

Frequency of updates: N/A

Search criteria available: Industry; Job category; Job type; Keyword; Location; Posting date

Resume database available: Yes

Employer profiles available: Yes

Costs for jobseekers to view jobs/ post a resume: Free

Costs for employers to list job openings/ view resumes: This is a fee-based service. Please visit the site for pricing information.

Other key features: Email service notifies jobseekers of new job listings; links to career fairs information; links to related career sites; and links to news and educational programs.

Insider tips: This site, which is connected to *Science* magazine, offers a very detailed search option, and has a decent number of job listings and company profiles for a relatively limited audience.

CHARITIES & SOCIAL SERVICES

THE NONPROFIT TIMES ONLINE

http://www.nptimes.com/classified.html
Types of jobs: Charities/Social Services/Nonprofit
Locations of jobs: United States
Frequency of updates: Monthly
Search criteria available: None
Resume database available: No
Employer profiles available: No
Insider tips: The company that operates this site also publishes a periodical. A one year subscription (18 issues) costs $59.

SOCIALSERVICE.COM

http://www.socialservice.com
Number of job listings: N/A
Types of jobs: Social Service
Locations of jobs: United States
Frequency of updates: N/A
Search criteria available: Location
Resume database available: No
Employer profiles available: No
Costs for jobseekers to view jobs/ post a resume: Free; N/A
Costs for employers to list job openings/ view resumes: $25/ad, which is listed under your state for three weeks. Ads are also emailed to candidates in the employer's state. Resumes are not available.
Other key features: Links to local job sites, as well as sites with resume databases; an **email service** which notifies jobseekers of new listings in their state; and detailed job listings.
Insider tips: A good source for narrowing your search for social service jobs to a particular geographic area.

SOCIAL WORK AND SOCIAL SERVICES JOBS ONLINE

http://www.gwbweb.wustl.edu/jobs/index.html
Number of job listings: N/A
Types of jobs: Social Services
Locations of jobs: United States and some international
Frequency of updates: N/A
Search criteria available: Location
Resume database available: N/A
Employer profiles available: No
Costs for jobseekers to view jobs/ post a resume: Free; N/A
Costs for employers to list job openings/ view resumes: N/A
Other key features: Links to local sites.
Insider tips: This site is a service of the George Warren Brown School of Social Work (St. Louis, MO). This site links with the school's Career Services site, which includes a database of "mini-resumes", and information on services and events.

COMMUNICATIONS

AIRWAVES MEDIA WEB

http://www.airwaves.com/job.html
Number of jobs listings: N/A
Types of jobs: Communications (Broadcast radio and related fields)
Locations of jobs: United States
Frequency of updates: N/A
Search criteria available: None
Resume database available: No (there is a "Positions Wanted" section)
Employer profiles available: No

THE JOBZONE

http://www.internettelephony.com/JobZone/jobzone.asp
Number of jobs listings: N/A
Types of jobs: Telecommunications
Locations of jobs: United States
Frequency of updates: N/A
Search criteria available: Company name; Job category; Keyword; Location
Resume database available: No
Employer profiles available: No
Costs for jobseekers to view jobs/ post a resume: Free; N/A
Costs for employers to list job openings/ view resumes: Prices vary for advertisers and non-advertisers, and decrease with the number of posted ads. For example, non-advertisers pay $200/posting, or $165/posting when 6-12 ads are posted. Advertisers would pay $120 and $102 per posting, respectively. Resumes are not available.
Other key features: Links to other telecom sites.
Insider tips: This site is a good, basic job search site; however, the job listings we found did not include posting dates, so you may want to contact the listed company to make sure the ad is current.

COMPUTERS

COMPUTER

http://www.computer.org/computer/career/career.htm
Number of job listings: N/A
Types of jobs: Computers/Education
Locations of jobs: United States and some international
Frequency of updates: Monthly
Search criteria available: N/A
Resume database available: No
Employer profiles available: No
Insider tips: This site is a service of *Computer* magazine.

THE COMPUTER JOBS STORE

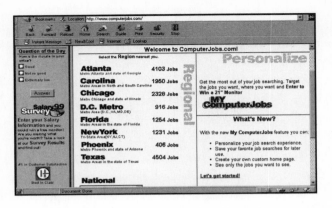

http://www.computerjobs.com

Number of job listings: 5,000 (at the national site)

Types of jobs: Computer

Locations of jobs: United States (individual state and city sites are also listed here)

Frequency of updates: Hourly

Search criteria available: Keyword; Location

Resume database available: Yes (registration required)

Employer profiles available: Yes

Costs for jobseekers to view jobs/ post a resume: Free

Costs for employers to list job openings/ view resumes: N/A

Other key features: Offers salary information and allows jobseekers to save their job search results.

Insider tips: This site links you to all of the different Computer Jobs Stores: Atlanta; Carolina; Chicago; D.C. Metro; Florida; New York; Phoenix; Texas; and National, which lists jobs for all areas of the U.S. not otherwise covered. Each site lists between 400 (Phoenix) and 4,500 (Texas) jobs.

COMPUTERWORK.COM

http://www.computerwork.com

Number of job listings: 10,000

Types of jobs: Computer

Locations of jobs: United States and Canada

Frequency of updates: Daily

Search criteria available: Job category; Keyword; Location; Posting date; Job type

Resume database available: Yes

Employer profiles available: Yes

Costs for jobseekers to view jobs/ post a resume: Free

Costs for employers to list job openings/ view resumes: A free, 30-day trial was being offered at the time of this writing. Contact Computerwork for additional pricing information.

Other key features: Links to related sites and a "Career Resources" section that offers the following: computer training information; career fairs information; career news; reference articles; and more.

Insider tips: Check out the "Other Sites" section for links to sites targeted at specific geographic and professional areas.

DICE.COM

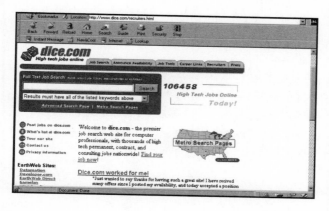

http://www.dice.com

Number of job listings: 106,000

Types of jobs listed: High tech

Locations of jobs: United States (metro areas)

Frequency of updates: N/A

Search criteria available: Keyword; Location; Job type; Area code; Posting date

Resume database available: Yes

Employer profiles available: Yes

Costs for jobseekers to view jobs/ post a resume: Free

Costs for employers to list job openings/ view resumes: Pricing plans range from $395 - $595 per month for unlimited postings, and allows access to candidate profiles.

Other key features: An **email service** notifying jobseekers of new listings matching specified criteria; relocation information; an "Announce Availability" feature that jobseekers fill out, and dice.com then sends via email to member companies; and listings are posted to other job sites as well, such as Yahoo! Classifieds.

Insider tips: In a four month period during our research, we saw the number of jobs posted at this site climb by nearly 35,000.

DIGITAL CAT'S HUMAN RESOURCE CENTER

http://www.jobcats.com
Number of job listings: N/A
Types of jobs: Computer
Locations of jobs: United States and some international
Frequency of updates: N/A
Search criteria available: Location; Skills
Resume database available: No
Employer profiles available: Yes

IDEAS JOB NETWORK

http://www.ideasjn.com
Number of job listings: N/A
Types of jobs: Computer/Engineering
Locations of jobs: United States and some international
Frequency of updates: N/A
Search criteria available: Location
Resume database available: No
Employer profiles available: No

1-JOBS.COM

http://www.1-jobs.com

Number of job listings: N/A

Types of jobs: Computers (Engineering and Telecommunications)

Locations of jobs: United States and some international

Frequency of updates: N/A

Search criteria available: Company name; Job category; Keyword; Location; Posting date

Resume database available: Yes

Employer profiles available: Yes

Costs for jobseekers to view jobs/ post a resume: Free (password required)

Costs for employers to list job openings/ view resumes: This is a fee-based service. Please contact 1-Jobs.com for pricing information.

Other key features: A schedule of high tech career fairs; links to tons of career sites, including city and state sites, association sites, newsgroups, online newspapers, and many more; registered jobseekers get a free subscription to *TechJobs* magazine; a free newsletter for registered employers; and more.

Insider tips: A must see for anybody interested in this particular field.

INFOWORKS USA

http://www.infoworksusa.com

Number of job listings: N/A

Types of jobs: Computer

Locations of jobs: United States

Frequency of updates: N/A

Search criteria available: Company name; Job title; Job type; Location

Resume database available: Yes

Employer profiles available: Yes

Costs for jobseekers to view jobs/ post a resume: Free

Costs for employers to list job openings/ view resumes: Please contact infoworks for pricing information.

Other key features: Profiles of member employees and featured companies, and a "skills quiz."

Insider tips: Visit the "Featured Companies" section to links to hundreds of top companies.

JOBS FOR PROGRAMMERS

http://www.prgjobs.com

Number of job listings: N/A

Types of jobs: Computer Programming

Locations of jobs: United States

Frequency of updates: N/A

Search criteria available: Keyword; Location; and numerous other qualifiers, including benefits, dress code, work schedule, and more.

Resume database available: Yes (30,000)

Employer profiles available: No

Costs for jobseekers to view jobs/ post a resume: Free

Costs for employers to list job openings/ view resumes: A free 30-day trial was being offered at the time of this writing, and covered both job postings and resume access. Please contact the site for more pricing information.

Other key features: Very detailed job descriptions.

JOBS.INTERNET.COM

http://jobs.internet.com
Number of job listings: N/A
Types of jobs: Computer
Locations of jobs: United States
Frequency of updates: Daily
Search criteria available: Job category; Keyword; Location; Salary
Resume database available: N/A
Employer profiles available: N/A
Costs for jobseekers to view jobs/ post a resume: Free; N/A
Costs for employers to list job openings/ view resumes: Postings at this site are listed through the CareerBuilder Network. Resumes are not available. Please visit the site for more information.

Other key features: An **email service** that notifies jobseekers of new listings matching their criteria; "Job of the Week" listing on homepage; links to various Internet resources, including a news section with articles on "Internet Careers"; and links to sites under the heading "internet.commerce" (banking, e-commerce, and others).

Insider tips: This site enjoys a partnership with the CareerBuilder Network, which offers broad Web exposure and more efficient job search/ employee search capabilities.

JOB WAREHOUSE

http://www.jobwarehouse.com
Number of job listings: 4,600
Types of jobs: Computer/ IT
Locations of jobs: United States and some international
Frequency of updates: N/A
Search criteria available: Company name; Keyword; Location; Job ID number; Posting date
Resume database available: Yes

Employer profiles available: Yes

Costs for jobseekers to view jobs/ post a resume: Free

Costs for employers to list job openings/ view resumes: This is a fee-based service. Please contact Job Warehouse for pricing information.

Other key features: Links to helpful sites for jobseekers, with topics ranging from salary information to tax rates; and an **email service** which notifies jobseekers of new opportunities, and notifies employers of newly-listed resumes matching their requirements.

Insider tips: A basic IT job site geared at serving both the jobseeker and the employer. If you want to get right to the job or resume listings, and bypass the extras some other sites have, this is a site you'll want to visit.

MACTALENT

http://www.mactalent.com

Number of job listings: N/A

Types of jobs: Computer (specifically Macintosh computer skills)

Locations of jobs: United States and some international

Frequency of updates: Daily

Search criteria available: None

Resume database available: Yes

Employer profiles available: No

Costs for jobseekers to view jobs/ post a resume: Free

Costs for employers to list job openings/ view resumes: Free

SELECTJOBS

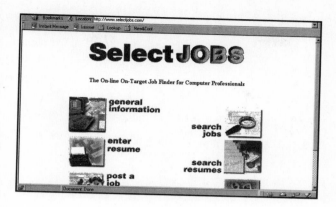

http://www.selectjobs.com

Number of job listings: 17,000

Types of jobs: Computer and high-tech industries, including positions in technical sales and marketing and technical recruiting

Locations of jobs: United States and some international

Frequency of updates: Daily

Search criteria available: Location; Skills; Keyword; Job title; Job category; Job type (full-time or contract position)

Resume database available: Yes

Employer profiles available: Yes

Costs for jobseekers to view jobs/ post a resume: Free

Costs for employers to list job openings/ view resumes: Rates vary from $100/month for one job listing, to a multi-listing plan (up to 250 positions) for $350-$400/month. These fees include job postings, resume search, a resume-match email service, and cross-posting to other Internet career sites.

Other key features: Automatic **email notification** of job matches; links to other career resource sites.

Insider tips: An extensive site for the computer industry since 1996, SelectJOBS has teamed up with nine other Internet career sites. The site won't send your resume to a company unless you've given your approval to do so.

TECHIES.COM

http://www.techies.com

Number of job listings: N/A

Types of jobs: High tech/ IT

Locations of jobs: Austin; Boston; Chicago; Dallas; Denver; Phoenix; Portland (OR); Seattle; Minneapolis/ St. Paul; and several other metro areas are scheduled to open

Frequency of updates: N/A

Search criteria available: Company name; Job category; Job title; Location

Resume database available: Yes

Employer profiles available: Yes

Costs for jobseekers to view jobs/ post a resume: Free (password required)

Costs for employers to list job openings/ view resumes: Two subscription plans are available: techies.com Network, and techies.com Premier Network. Please contact techies.com for pricing information.

Insider tips: This site continues to add more cities to its list. Check out the site for the latest additions, and if you don't find what you're looking for, reply to the "Don't see your city?" section of the homepage. You can indicate your interest in a new site for your city, and techies.com will notify if/when it is developed.

ACADEMIC EMPLOYMENT NETWORK

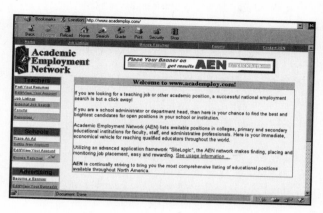

http://www.academploy.com

Number of job listings: 60

Types of jobs: Teaching and other academic positions

Locations of jobs: United States and Canada

Frequency of updates: N/A

Search criteria available: Location

Resume database available: Yes

Employer profiles available: N/A

Costs for jobseekers to view jobs/ post a resume: N/A

Costs for employers to list job openings/ view resumes: Schools or academic institutions need an annual subscription with the Academic Employment Network to access the resume database.

Other key features: Links to education-related Websites, relocation services, and certification and development resources, as well as its own forum.

Insider tips: A small site that is easy to navigate and offers a good deal of useful information for the jobseeker focused on academics. Positions are posted for 30 days.

ACADEMIC POSITION NETWORK

http://www.apnjobs.com
Number of job listings: N/A
Types of jobs: Education
Locations of jobs: United States and some international
Frequency of updates: Daily
Search criteria available: Field of Interest; Job type; Institution type
Resume database available: No
Employer profiles available: No

AECT PLACEMENT CENTER

http://www.aect.org/employment/employment.htm
Number of job listings: N/A
Types of jobs: Education; Technical
Locations of jobs: United States
Frequency of updates: Monthly
Search criteria available: Positions can be searched by preset application deadlines.
Resume database available: No
Employer profiles available: No
Costs for jobseekers to view jobs/ post a resume: Free; N/A
Costs for employers to list job openings/ view resumes: Free; N/A
Insider tips: Most positions listed are within an academic institution.

THE CHRONICLE OF HIGHER EDUCATION/ CAREER NETWORK

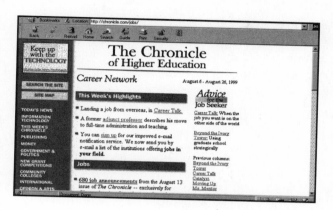

http://chronicle.com/jobs

Number of job listings: 1,600

Types of jobs: Academic, both faculty and nonfaculty available

Locations of jobs: United States and some international

Frequency of updates: Weekly

Search criteria available: Job category (and subsets within categories), keyword, and region

Resume Database available: N/A

Employer profiles available: N/A

Costs for jobseekers to view jobs/ post a resume: About 800 of the 1,600 listings are accessible to subscribers only, which costs $75 per year. International rates vary.

Costs for employers to list job openings/ view resumes: N/A

Other key features: Subscribers can see the full text of *The Chronicle of Higher Education*, the trade newspaper for academics.

Insider tips: The Career Network contains hundreds of listings for faculty, administrative, and executive positions for prestigious U.S. colleges. The job database includes listings for related positions outside of academe, in organizations such as art galleries, government agencies, museums, and other nonprofit organizations.

DAVE'S ESL CAFE

http://www.eslcafe.com
Number of job listings: N/A
Types of jobs: Education (English as a Second Language teaching jobs)
Locations of jobs: United States and Korea
Frequency of updates: Daily
Search criteria available: Location
Resume database available: No (but there is a "Job Wanted Board" used by jobseekers)
Employer profiles available: No
Other key features: English as a Second Language (ESL) and English as a Foreign Language (EFL) worldwide job listings, and an area specifically for Korean jobs; links to other ESL and EFL online resources; and forums on teacher training and ESL /EFL jobs.

HIGHEREDJOBS ONLINE

http://www.higheredjobs.com
Number of job listings: N/A
Types of jobs: Education
Locations of jobs: United States
Frequency of updates: N/A
Search criteria available: Company name; Job category; Job title; Location
Resume database available: No
Employer profiles available: No
Costs for jobseekers to view jobs/ post a resume: Free; N/A
Costs for employers to list job openings/ view resumes: $75/ad/up to three months for non-subscribers. Please visit the site for more details. Resumes are not available.
Other key features: A free subscription to Higher Ed Jobs Online, offered to educational institutions (restrictions apply); and an **email service** that sends occasional updates to registered jobseekers, detailing information on newly-listed educational institutions and more.
Insider tips: As the name suggests, this site lists information for institutions of higher education only. Jobseekers can search for staff or faculty positions, or by state or institution.

JOBS IN HIGHER EDUCATION

http://www.gslis.utexas.edu/~acadres/jobs/index.html
Number of job listings: N/A
Types of jobs: Education
Locations of jobs: United States; Australia; Canada; United Kingdom
Frequency of updates: N/A
Search criteria available: Company name; Job category; Job title; Location
Resume database available: No
Employer profiles available: Yes
Costs for jobseekers to view jobs/ post a resume: Free; N/A
Costs for employers to list job openings/ view resumes: N/A
Other key features: Links to topical or geographic sites; access to related newsgroups; and a listing of relevant associations.
Insider tips: At the time of this writing, the site had links to more than 1,450 institutions of higher learning.

LIBRARY & INFORMATION SCIENCE JOBSEARCH

http://www.carousel.lis.uiuc.edu/~jobs
Number of jobs listings: 775
Types of jobs: Education
Locations of jobs: United States
Frequency of updates: N/A
Search criteria available: Company name; Job category; Job title; Keyword; Location; Skills; Posting date
Resume database available: No
Employer profiles available: Yes
Insider tips: Job categories include Acquisitions, Archives, Business, Cataloging, Circulation, Indexing & Abstracting, Music Librarian, Reference, Serials, and many others.

THE PRIVATE SCHOOL
EMPLOYMENT NETWORK

http://www.privateschooljobs.com
Number of job listings: N/A
Types of jobs: Education
Locations of jobs: United States
Frequency of updates: N/A
Search criteria available: Job category; Job title
Resume database available: Yes
Employer profiles available: N/A
Costs for jobseekers to view jobs/ post a resume: There is no fee to view jobs. There is a $25 fee for posting a resume.
Costs for employers to list job openings/ view resumes: $75 for one posting, $125 for two postings, and $150 for three postings. Please contact the site for additional pricing options. Resume access is free.

TEACHER JOBS

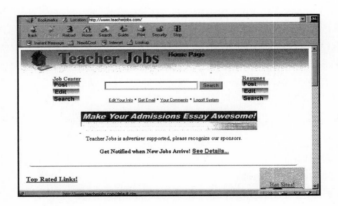

http://www.teacherjobs.com
Types of jobs: Education
Locations of jobs: United States (including Puerto Rico)
Search criteria available: Job category; Job title; Location
Resume database available: Yes
Employer profiles available: Yes
Costs for jobseekers to view jobs/ post a resume: Free

Costs for employers to list job openings/ view resumes: Free

Insider tips: Registration is required (free).

ENGINEERING

ENGINEERJOBS.COM

http://www.engineerjobs.com

Number of job listings: N/A

Types of jobs: Engineering

Locations of jobs: United States, with an emphasis on the Great Lakes area

Frequency of updates: N/A

Search criteria available: Keyword; Location

Resume database available: Yes

Employer profiles available: No

Costs for jobseekers to view jobs/ post a resume: Free

Costs for employers to list job openings/ view resumes: $30/listing for 30 days, or $600/100 listings for two months, or $3000/1,200 listings for one year. Other advertising packages are available. Resume access is included in payment for jobs listings.

Other key features: An **email service** for jobseekers; very detailed job descriptions; links to other engineering and technical sites.

Insider tips: This is one of the more popular and resourceful sites related to engineering jobs, and is working to expand its services nationwide.

ENVIRONMENTAL

ECOLOGIC

http://www.rpi.edu/dept/union/pugwash/ecojobs.htm

Types of jobs: Environmental

Locations of jobs: N/A

Insider tips: This site, a service of Rensselaer Student Pugwash, Rensselaer Polytechnic Institute, does not list job openings, but does offer links to environmental career sites.

ENVIRONMENTAL JOBS SEARCH PAGE!

http://ourworld.compuserve.com/homepages/ubikk/env4.htm
Types of jobs: Environmental, including: Administration/Clerical; Computers; Construction/Engineering/Design; Managerial/Executive/Consulting; Scientific; and others.
Locations of jobs: United States and Canada
Search criteria available: Company name; Industry; Job category; Job title
Insider tips: You'll find job searching tips, GIS information, internship information, and more at this site. A job search on this page will directly link you to the E Jobs employment page.

WATER ENVIRONMENT WEB

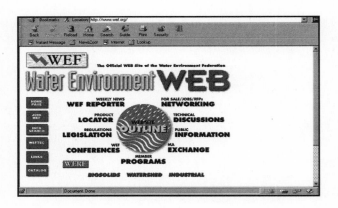

http://www.wef.org
Types of jobs: Environmental
Locations of jobs: United States
Search criteria available: Job title; Location
Resume database available: No
Employer profiles available: No
Insider tips: This site is a service of the Water Environment Federation.

GOVERNMENT

CORPORATE GRAY ONLINE

http://www.greentogray.com
Insider tips: This site is offered as a career resource to military personnel leaving the service.

FEDERAL JOBS CENTRAL

http://www.fedjobs.com
Number of job listings: N/A
Types of jobs: Federal Government
Locations of jobs: United States
Frequency of updates: Daily
Search criteria available: Industry; Job category; Job title; Keyword; Location; Skills; Salary
Resume database available: No
Employer profiles available: No
Costs for jobseekers to view jobs/ post a resume: $19.97/month for unlimited usage, or $49 for three months. Resumes are not available.
Costs for employers to list job openings/ view resumes: N/A
Other key features: A calender of events; career tips; information on Federal agencies; and more.
Insider tips: Posted positions are listed exclusively on this site.

FEDERAL JOBS DIGEST

http://www.jobsfed.com
Number of job listings: 9,300
Types of jobs: Government (all levels)
Locations of jobs: United States
Frequency of updates: Daily
Search criteria available: Job category; Job title; Location
Resume database available: Yes
Employer profiles available: No
Costs for jobseekers to view jobs/ post a resume: Free

Costs for employers to list job openings/ view resumes: Free

Other key features: A detailed resume posting area; a listing of the most recent job postings; a jobs bulletin board; listing of hotlines; a "job matching service"; and information on Federal benefits.

Insider tips: Government and private sector employers can place job listings here, free of charge.

FEDWORLD FEDERAL JOB ANNOUNCEMENT SEARCH

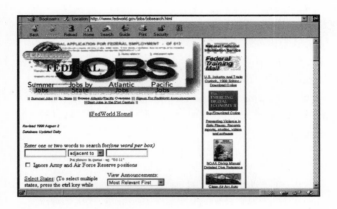

http://www.fedworld.gov/jobs/jobsearch.html

Number of job listings: N/A

Types of jobs: All

Locations of jobs: United States and some U.S. territories

Frequency of updates: Daily

Search criteria available: Keyword; Location; Summer Jobs

Resume database available: No

Employer profiles available: N/A

Costs for jobseekers to view jobs/ post a resume: Free; N/A

Costs for employers to list job openings/ view resumes: N/A

Other key features: Includes links to numerous other sites and access to various government databases, such as the FedWorld File Libraries, where you can find archival information on business, the environment, and many other subjects. You can also find and order information from the U.S. government.

Insider tips: This site is brought to you courtesy of the National Technical Information Services (NTIS), an agency of the U.S. Department of Commerce.

The jobs database contains openings for all kinds of positions, from computer analyst to maintenance.

THE POLICE OFFICERS INTERNET DIRECTORY

http://www.officer.com/jobs.htm
Number of job listings: N/A
Types of jobs: Law enforcement
Locations of jobs: United States
Frequency of updates: N/A
Search criteria available: Location
Resume database available: N/A
Employer profiles available: N/A
Costs for jobseekers to view jobs/ post a resume: Free; N/A
Costs for employers to list job openings/ view resumes: N/A
Other key features: Links to related sites, such as Cops 2 Be and Cop Spot Employment.
Insider tips: This site doesn't list job openings, rather it provides links to law enforcement sites that do list jobs and related information.

HEALTH CARE

AMERICA'S HEALTH CARE SOURCE

http://www.healthcaresource.com
Number of job listings: N/A
Types of jobs: Health care
Locations of jobs: United States
Frequency of updates: N/A
Search criteria available: Industry; Job category; Job title; Location
Resume database available: Yes
Employer profiles available: No

HEALTHBANK USA

http://www.healthbankusa.com
Number of job listings: N/A
Types of jobs: Healthcare
Locations of jobs: United States
Frequency of updates: N/A
Search criteria available: Job category; Job title
Resume database available: Yes
Employer profiles available: No
Costs for jobseekers to view jobs/ post a resume: Free
Costs for employers to list job openings/ view resumes: $75/ad for 60 days, or $395 per month for an unlimited number of postings. Resume access is included in these payment plans.

HEALTH CAREER WEB

http://www.healthcareerweb.com
Number of job listings: N/A
Types of jobs: Health care
Locations of jobs: United States
Frequency of updates: N/A
Search criteria available: Job category; Keyword; Location
Resume database available: Yes
Employer profiles available: Yes
Costs for jobseekers to view jobs/ post a resume: Free
Costs for employers to list job openings/ view resumes: $160/ad for 60 days, or $7,500 for an unlimited number of ads for one year. Please contact the site for details on other pricing options. There is no charge to access resumes.
Other key features: Career articles and advice; an **email service** for job-seekers; links to career books; and more.
Insider tips: This is CareerWeb's health care site. The company profiles are very thorough.

HEALTH CARE JOBS ONLINE

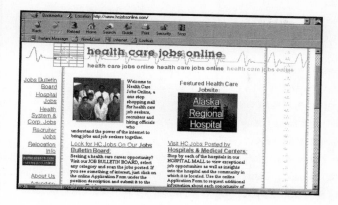

http://www.hcjobsonline.com
Number of job listings: N/A
Types of jobs: Health care
Locations of jobs: United States
Frequency of updates: N/A
Search criteria available: Job category; Keyword
Resume database available: No
Employer profiles available: Yes
Costs for jobseekers to view jobs/ post a resume: Free; N/A
Costs for employers to list job openings/ view resumes: $50/month/category, and $10/month for each additional category. Ads can be renewed for 31 days for $25. Resumes are not available.
Other key features: Links to health care and career related sites, including salary and relocation information.
Insider tips: Job categories include: Nursing, Therapies, Physicians, Pharmacy, Lab, Administrative, Financial, HC Marketing, and Other.

HEALTH CARE RECRUITMENT ONLINE

http://www.healthcarerecruitment.com
Number of job listings: N/A
Types of jobs: Health care
Locations of jobs: United States
Frequency of updates: N/A

Resume database available: No
Employer profiles available: Yes

MEDHUNTERS

http://www.medhunters.com
Number of job listings: N/A
Types of jobs: Health care
Locations of jobs: United States and some international
Frequency of updates: N/A
Search criteria available: Job title; Keyword; Location
Resume database available: Yes
Employer profiles available: Yes

MEDICAL-ADMART

http://www.medical-admart.com
Number of job postings: 1,000
Types of jobs: Health care
Locations of jobs: United States
Frequency of updates: N/A
Search criteria available: Job category
Resume database available: No
Employer profiles available: No
Costs for jobseekers to view jobs/ post a resume: Free; N/A
Costs for employers to list job openings/ view resumes: Varies according to publication. Please visit the site for pricing information. Resumes are not available.
Other key features: Links to related sites.
Insider tips: This site lists health care/ medical publications, and offers links to each. Job postings are at the individual sites.

MEDICAL DEVICE LINK

http://www.devicelink.com/career
Number of job listings: N/A

Types of jobs: Medical (includes engineering, computers, research, and others)

Locations of jobs: United States

Frequency of updates: Daily

Search criteria available: N/A

Resume database available: Yes

Employer profiles available: No (though addresses and product information are listed under the heading "Suppliers")

MEDZILLA

http://www.medzilla.com

Number of job listings: N/A

Types of jobs: Biotechnology, health care, and medical

Locations of jobs: United States

Frequency of updates: N/A

Search criteria available: Keyword

Resume database available: Yes

Employer profiles available: Yes

Costs for jobseekers to view jobs/ post a resume: Free

Costs for employers to list job openings/ view resumes: $95/month per job posting, or $250/month for an unlimited number of job postings. Resumes may be viewed free of charge.

Other key features: Links to employer Websites, and articles on job searching as well as the health care industry.

Insider tips: A small but helpful resource for job seekers in health care and related fields. Some listings include extensive employer descriptions and an area set up to automatically email the employee.

NURSING SPECTRUM CAREER FITNESS ONLINE

http://www.nursingspectrum.com

Number of job listings: N/A

Types of jobs: Nursing (Registered Nurses)

Locations of jobs: United States (particularly the Eastern states)

Frequency of updates: N/A

Search criteria available: Industry; Job category; Keyword; Location
Resume database available: No
Employer profiles available: Yes
Costs for jobseekers to view jobs/ post a resume: Free; N/A
Costs for employers to list job openings/ view resumes: Free; N/A
Other key features: A schedule of nationwide nursing events; a chat area; nursing forum; and other resources, including nursing books, health care policy information, and educational resources.
Insider tips: Check this site out if you have any interest in nursing – whether you're looking for a new job, looking for a new employee, or you're simply interested in staying informed, or learning more about, the nursing profession.

PHYSICIANS EMPLOYMENT

http://www.physemp.com
Number of job listings: 2,000
Types of jobs: Health care (physicians, nurses, allied health professionals)
Locations of jobs: United States
Frequency of updates: N/A
Search criteria available: Job category; Location
Resume database available: No
Employer profiles available: No
Costs for jobseekers to view jobs/ post a resume: Free; N/A
Costs for employers to list job openings/ view resumes: N/A
Other key features: N/A
Insider tips: This is one of the Web's largest and oldest job sites devoted to health care.

SALUDOS HISPANIS WEB
CAREER CENTER

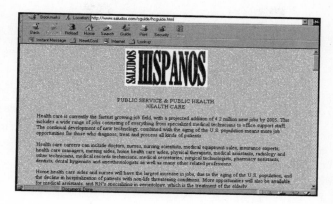

http://www.saludos.com/cguide/hcguide.html

Types of jobs: Health care (and others)

Locations of jobs: United States

Search criteria available: Job category; Job title

Resume database available: Yes

Employer profiles available: No

Costs for jobseekers to view jobs/ post a resume: Free

Costs for employers to list job openings/ view resumes: $99/month per job listing, or $129 for two months. Corporate packages are available. Only paying members can access resumes.

HOTELS & RESTAURANTS

ESCOFFIER ONLINE

http://www.escoffier.com/nonscape/employ.shtml

Types of jobs: Hotel and Restaurant

Locations of jobs: United States

Search criteria available: Job title

Resume database available: Yes

Employer profiles available: No
Costs for jobseekers to view jobs/ post a resume: Free
Costs for employers to list job openings/ view resumes: Free

HUMAN RESOURCES/ RECRUITING

HR WORLD

http://www.hrworld.com
Number of job listings: N/A
Types of jobs: Human Resources
Locations of jobs: United States
Frequency of updates: N/A
Search criteria available: Job title; Location
Resume database available: No
Employer profiles available: No
Costs for jobseekers to view jobs/ post a resume: Free; N/A
Costs for employers to list job openings/ view resumes: Free; N/A
Other key features: Forums; information on human resources products and services; access to human resources articles and publications; and links to worldwide human resources sites.

JOBS 4 HR

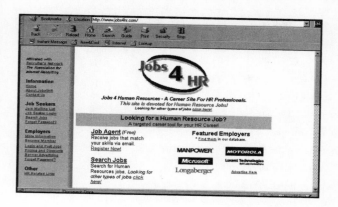

http://www.jobs4hr.com

Number of job listings: N/A

Types of jobs: Human Resources

Locations of jobs: United States

Frequency of updates: N/A

Search criteria available: Company name; Job category; Keyword; Location

Resume database available: No

Employer profiles available: No

Costs for jobseekers to view jobs/ post a resume: Free; N/A

Costs for employers to list job openings/ view resumes: $100/ad, $350/5 ads, $600/10 ads, $800/unlimited postings for three months, or $1,750/unlimited postings for one year.

Other key features: A free **email "Job Agent"** that notifies jobseekers of new listings matching their chosen criteria; a mailing list connecting jobseekers and employers; and links to other HR sites.

Insider tips: Employers that use this site include Microsoft, Lucent Technologies, Manpower, and many others. Jobs 4 HR is operated by Recruiter's Network.

INSURANCE

THE INSURANCE CAREER CENTER

http://www.connectyou.com/talent
Number of job listings: N/A
Types of jobs: Insurance
Locations of jobs: United States
Frequency of updates: Daily
Search criteria available: Company name; Job category; Job title; Location
Resume database available: Yes
Employer profiles available: Yes
Costs for jobseekers to view jobs/ post a resume: Free
Costs for employers to list job openings/ view resumes: $160/posting for 30 days. The "Position Wanted" section can be accessed free of charge, but there is a fee to access the resume database. Please contact the site for pricing information.
Insider tips: This site is a service of CareerMosaic.

INSURANCE NATIONAL SEARCH

http://www.insurancerecruiters.com/insjobs/jobs.htm
Number of job listings: N/A
Types of jobs: Insurance, with positions in: Accounting; Actuary; Administrative and Executive; Claims; Clerical/Secretarial; Human Resources; Information Systems; Investment; Legal; Marketing and Communications; Pension; Policyholder Services; Safety and Loss Control; Sales; Underwriting; and miscellaneous.
Locations of jobs: United States
Frequency of updates: Weekly
Search criteria available: Job category; Job title; Keyword
Resume database available: No
Employer profiles available: No
Other key features: Links to other career sites and a schedule of events in the insurance industry; information on insurance associations, discussion groups, and news; and areas to learn about insurance and related terminology.

Insider tips: This site offers jobs from, and contact with, a nationwide network of recruiters.

L E G A L

LAW NEWS NETWORK.COM

http://www.lawjobs.com

Number of job listings: N/A

Types of jobs: Legal

Locations of jobs: United States, with a focus on the following: CA, CT, FL, GA, NJ, NY, PA, TX, and DC.

Frequency of updates: N/A

Search criteria available: Job title; Location

Resume database available: No

Employer profiles available: No

Costs for jobseekers to view jobs/ post a resume: Free; N/A

Costs for employers to list job openings/ view resumes: Prices vary with location. Please visit the site for more information. Resumes are not available.

Other key features: List of recruiters from each state and international recruiters; email service allows jobseekers to easily send postings to friends and colleagues; and links to temporary agencies, regional classified ads, and related news.

Insider tips: This site is a service of American Lawyer Media, which prints newspapers and journals.

THE LEGAL EMPLOYMENT SEARCH SITE

http://www.legalemploy.com
Types of jobs: Legal
Locations of jobs: United States
Search criteria available: None
Insider tips: This site does not offer job listings, but it does offer hundreds of links to Websites devoted to the legal profession, as well as links to employment services and general job search sites.

RIGHT OF WAY EMPLOYMENT JOBLINE

http://www.rightofway.com/jobline.html
Types of jobs: Land/Property Acquisition
Locations of jobs: United States
Search criteria available: N/A
Resume database available: Yes
Employer profiles available: No
Costs for jobseekers to view jobs/ post a resume: Free; N/A
Costs for employers to list job openings/ view resumes: Free; N/A

MINING/GAS/ PETROLEUM

OIL-LINK

http://www.oillink.com
Number of job listings: N/A
Types of jobs: Mining/Gas/Petroleum/Energy related
Locations of jobs: United States
Frequency of updates: N/A
Search criteria available: Company name; Job title; Keyword
Resume database available: Yes

Employer profiles available: Yes

Costs for jobseekers to view jobs/ post a resume: Free

Costs for employers to list job openings/ view resumes: $125/60 days. Resumes may be accessed free of charge.

Other key features: Lots of industry information, including news, surveys, stats, books, and more; links to all sorts of Web resources – newsgroups, government sites, events schedules, educational information, associations, and listings for different oil and gas categories; and "Inbox Direct," a free, daily newsletter **sent to you via e-mail**, that details current news and offers new job listings.

Insider tips: For oil and gas jobs, this is a big site. The site reports 120,000 visits per month, by 38,000 unique users. Companies that post listings include: Texaco, Schlumberger, Hunt Oil Company, and many more.

PRINTING & PUBLISHING

JOBLINK FOR JOURNALISTS

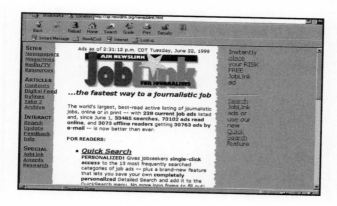

http://ajr.newslink.org/newjoblink.html

Number of job listings: 180

Types of jobs: Journalism

Locations of jobs: United States

Frequency of updates: N/A

Search criteria available: Industry; Job category; Job title; Keyword; Salary; Skills; Work environment

Resume database available: Yes
Employer profiles available: No
Costs for jobseekers to view jobs/ post a resume: Free
Costs for employers to list job openings/ view resumes: $49.95 for five weeks. Resumes may be accessed free of charge.
Other key features: Links to newspapers, magazines, and other media resources; related news articles; an **email notification service** for jobseekers; and a research section.

JOBS IN JOURNALISM

http://eb.journ.latech.edu/jobs.html
Number of job listings: N/A
Types of jobs: Journalism; Printing/Publishing
Locations of jobs: United States
Frequency of updates: N/A
Search criteria available: Archive date
Resume database available: No
Employer profiles available: No
Insider tips: Jobs are archived here, gathered each week from a journalism listserv.

RETAIL

RETAIL JOBNET

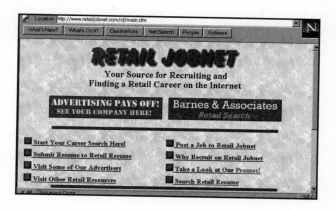

http://www.retailjobnet.com

Number of job listings: N/A

Types of jobs: Retail, in the specific areas of advertising, public relations, buying, field management, and human resources

Locations of jobs: United States

Frequency of updates: Weekly

Search criteria available: Location; Job category; Job title

Resume database available: Yes

Employer profiles available: Yes (very limited)

Costs for jobseekers to view jobs/ post a resume: Free

Costs for employers to list job openings/ view resumes: Rates vary – the basic plan is $139/month for one posting. Resumes may be accessed at the rate of $99/month or $599/year.

Other key features: Links to other retail sites.

Insider tips: This site is focused exclusively on positions in the retail industry, and continues to work diligently to add listings and sponsors. At the time of this writing, the site listed 680 resumes.

TRANSPORTATION

INTERNATIONAL SEAFARERS EXCHANGE

http://www.jobxchange.com/xisetoc.htm
Number of job listings: 325
Types of jobs: Cruise ship and Maritime positions
Locations of jobs: United States and some international
Search criteria available: Job category; Job title; Salary; Skills
Resume database available: Yes
Employer profiles available: No
Insider tips: Jobs can be searched from the following categories: Deck; Engineering; Offshore; Medical; Hotel; Housekeeping; Food & Beverage; Galley; Bar; Cruise Staff; Entertainment; Casino; Beauty Salon; Gift Shop; Photo Shop; Lecturers; Instructors; and Clergy

1-800-DRIVERS

http://204.32.45.41/final/seek.htm
Types of jobs: Drivers and Owner/Operators jobs in the transportation industry
Locations of jobs: United States and Canada
Search criteria available: Job category; Location; Skills; Trailer type
Resume database available: No
Employer profiles available: Yes
Insider tips: While this site does not offer specific job openings, it does provide links to company Web pages and applications for ongoing hiring.

UTILITIES

POWER

http://www.powermag.com
Number of job listings: N/A

Types of jobs: Utilities/Energy (includes jobs in engineering, computers, and many other disciplines)

Locations of jobs: United States and some international (Saudi Arabian listings were offered at the time of this writing)

Frequency of updates: N/A

Search criteria available: N/A

Resume database available: No

Employer profiles available: No

RESUME SITES

A+ Online Resumes

http://www.ol-resume.com

AAAA – Job Resume Services

http://www.aaaa-job.com

Acorn Career Counseling and Resume Writing

http://acornresume.com

CandidatePool

http://www.candidatepool.com

Employnet

http://www.employnet-inc.com

1st Impressions Resume & Career Strategies

http://www.1st-imp.com

HotResume

http://www.hotresume.com

JobDirect.com

http://www.jobdirect.com

#1 Resume Writing Services

http://www.free-resume-tips.com/index.html

OMICRONet Personal Career Center

http://www.omicronet.com/career/resume.htm

PursuitNet Online

http://www.tiac.net/users/jobs/index.html

ResumeBlaster

http://www.resumeblaster.com

Resume' Net

http://www.resumenet.com

The Resume Place

       http://www.resume-place.com

ResumeXPRESS

       http://www.resumexpress.com

Shawn's Internet Resume Center

       http://www.inpursuit.com/sirc

SkillBank

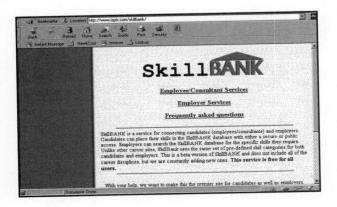

       http://www.lapis.com/skillbank

US Resume

       http://www.usresume.com

Search Engines

Another way to find job listings on the Web is to perform a keyword
search in a search engine such as Yahoo! or Lycos. Try using keywords
like "employment opportunities," "job listings," or "positions available."
A few of the most popular search engines include:

Yahoo!

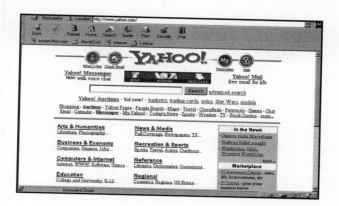

http://www.yahoo.com

Lycos

http://www.lycos.com

Excite

http://www.excite.com

Infoseek

http://infoseek.go.com

HotBot

http://www.hotbot.com

AltaVista

http://www.altavista.com

Go Network

http://www.go.com

Snap

http://www.snap.com

There are many, many more search engines available to you, offering various search capabilities, from Web-wide searches, to geographically-specific searches. A search for "search engines" on Yahoo!, for example, results in an extensive list of different search engines. We suggest focusing first on the Websites listed in this chapter, and then utilize a search engine if you need to find more information.

CHAPTER FIVE

GOPHER AND BULLETIN BOARD SYSTEMS

So far, we have recommended using commercial online services, newsgroups, and the World Wide Web to find job listings. Now we will examine two final pieces of the online puzzle, Gopher and Bulletin Board Systems (BBSs). While the obvious choice for finding the greatest number of job openings is the Web, Gopher and BBSs do offer thousands of job listings and other resources, including job search tips and company information. Some of the information is exclusive to these areas, and cannot be found on the Web. Gopher, in particular, remains a good source for specialized, high-quality job listings. **Note:** Due to its limited online presence, Telnet is no longer covered in this publication.

Gopher

Before the Web, there was Gopher. Named after the mascot at the University of Minnesota—where it was developed—**Gopher is often called the "grandparent technology" to the World Wide Web.** Gopher organizes its information into easy-to-use menus, which make navigating Gopherspace virtually effortless. Simply click on a menu choice which, like on the Web, is represented by underlined words, and you will be transported to that server. Unlike the Web, however, Gopher does *not* use hypertext links or graphics to convey information.

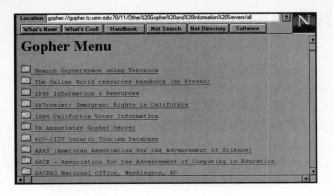

Users may connect to a Gopher server in several different ways: directly through their Internet provider, through their Web browser, or through a commercial online service. America Online in particular has an excellent Gopher connection, complete with a list of "Gopher Treasures" (keyword: **gopher**), a directory of the most interesting and informative sites available through Gopher.

Like the Web, Gopher contains thousands of sites providing a wide variety of information. You may, for instance, tune in to discover the latest political happenings at C-Span's Gopher server. Lists of all Gopher servers are found in three main directories (click on the "Gopher Directory" icon in AOL's Gopher site). Gopher Jewels (**Gopher://cwis.usc.edu/11/Other_Gophers_and_Information_Resources/Gophers_by_Subject/Gopher_Jewels**) organizes its list into subjects, as does Rice University's Gopher Directory (**Gopher://riceinfo.rice.edu/11/Subject**). Finally, All the Gopher Sites in the World (**Gopher://Gopher.tc.umn.edu/11/Other%20Gopher%20and%20Information%20Servers**), the root Gopher server at the University of Minnesota, is a list of every Gopher site available throughout the world, organized alphabetically or by continent. At the same time, it's easy to search through these vast directories with the help of the Gopher search engines Veronica and Jughead. Veronica is the bigger of the two, but both allow users to perform a keyword search to locate specific information, such as Gopher sites with job listings.

Since the advent of the World Wide Web, however, growth of Gopherspace has come to a virtual standstill. Few new Gopher sites are being created, and many are shutting down and reappearing as sites on the World Wide Web. Additionally, services that have been maintaining both a Gopher and Web presence are shutting down their Gopher servers in growing numbers.

But today, Gopher is still a viable source for job listings. Although you will not find the large, all-purpose job databases containing hundreds of thousands of job listings like those found on the Web, you will find thousands of job listings in a number of fields, particularly academia. Several colleges and universities post their job listings through Gopher, a reflection of the academic roots of the service. Users will also find job openings at the Library of Congress, and for such highly specialized jobs as economists and medical therapists. In fact, Gopher is one area where job hunters in traditional fields, such as computers, engineering, or finance, are likely to come up empty. **Note:** Much of the information available through Gopher is also available on the Web.

ARTJOB

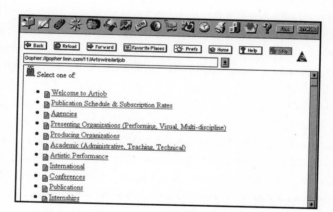

Gopher://gopher.tmn.com/11/Artswire/artjob

Number of job listings: N/A

Types of jobs: Positions in the arts, including theater, dance, opera, and museums

Locations of jobs: United States and some international

Frequency of updates: Biweekly

Search criteria available: Category

Key features: Includes information on internships, grants, competitions, and conferences

Insider tips: A service of the Western States Arts Federation, ArtJob is a rarity on the Internet—a site devoted to job listings in the arts. The positions are divided into four categories: presenting organizations, producing organizations, academic, and artistic performance. The jobs cover a wide spectrum of the arts—from a museum director in Roanoke, Virginia to silent comedic actors for a cruise line.

Bulletin Board Systems

Bulletin Board Systems are an often overlooked online resource for job listings. These days, it seems everyone is more interested in the World Wide Web and services like Monster.com or CareerMosaic. But job-related bulletin boards can contain thousands of job listings! To connect to a BBS, all you need is a computer, a modem, a telephone line, and communications software.

Bulletin Board Systems have been around since 1978. Basically, a BBS is a computer set up with special software that you access by using a regular telephone line and the communications software on your computer. They were created as a way for people to exchange information and discuss ideas, much like a Usenet newsgroup.

The bad news is that as the World Wide Web has continued to grow in popularity, BBSs have faded out. Even *Boardwatch* magazine, which once called itself "The Official Guide to Bulletin Board Systems," now goes by a broader subtitle, "The Guide to Internet Access and the World Wide Web."

That said, BBSs remain excellent sources of information, services, and entertainment. You can find millions of files available for downloading, including new freeware and shareware; you can participate in multi-user games; or you can simply chat with other users about various topics of interest.

The most frequent complaint against bulletin board systems continues to be the difficulty in finding out what Bulletin Board Systems exist in a particular area. If you have access to the World Wide Web, try a search engine like Yahoo! or a commercial online service like America Online to find bulletin boards in your area. Check out The BBS Corner (keyword: **BBS**) on AOL; it's also available on the Web (**http://www.thedirectory.org.**).

Besides job listings, employment-related BBSs may contain a resume database and online discussion area, and provide users with access to the Internet and Usenet newsgroups. And job hunters interested in finding technical positions, or jobs in federal, state, or local governments, should take special notice of the number of BBSs dedicated to those areas.

The following listings represent the extent of the employment-related BBSs we could unearth during production of this book, as well as the numbers to dial through your computer modem in order to access them. The most reliable sites are maintained by the federal government, and those are also available on the World Wide Web.

Connecting to a BBS is a simple process. Using Windows 95, for example, click on the "Start" menu, then click on "Programs". Put your cursor on "Accessories", and then move it down and click on "HyperTerminal". Follow that with a click on "Hypertrm.exe." You will then be asked to name the connection and choose an icon. The next prompt will ask you to enter the dial-up number for the BBS you want to access. Make sure to enter both the correct area code and seven digit phone number. Click on "Dial" on the following prompt, and you will then be connected to the BBS. **Note:** Similar communications software (like HyperTerminal on Windows 95) should be available on most systems.

After connecting to a new BBS, you will be required to register in order to use any of the services provided. This is done to discourage casual users from tying up the phone lines. Since most BBSs have only a limited number of phone lines (some may have only four or five), the system operators, or sysops, also limit the number of minutes users can spend on the system in one day.

Note: Remember that while these services are free, you will be charged the cost of a regular long-distance telephone call (if applicable) while you are connected to the BBS. For this reason, try calling during off-peak hours to minimize your phone bill.

Exec-PC
414-789-4210

This is an enormous BBS with thousands of files available for download, including job listings nationwide. Also contains local access numbers for users dialing long-distance. The Web address, which offers all the information from the BBS, is http://filepile.com.

Harry's Job Search BBS & Internet Hot List

This is not a BBS, but rather a detailed list of BBSs. The listings include name/location (including Web and Gopher access, if available), dial-up number, and notes about fees, type of BBS, and more. The Web address for this site is http://www.job-hunt.org/jobs-bbs.html.

OPM Mainstreet

202-606-4800

Includes federal job listings from the Office of Personnel Management, as well as access to other federal job BBSs and employment-related mailing lists and Usenet newsgroups.

CHAPTER SIX

RESEARCHING COMPANIES ONLINE

Investigating potential employers is critical to the job hunting process. Whether you are researching companies to target in your job search or trying to educate yourself about a potential employer's background, it is essential to have thorough, up-to-date information about your target companies. And one of the the best ways to find this information is to use the World Wide Web. Employer profiles are popping up on an increasing number of job sites, and more and more companies are constructing their own Websites, complete with hiring information and employment listings.

Creating Your Target List of Companies

Advance research is essential in any job hunt. Otherwise, you could waste time sending resumes to companies that haven't hired for your position in years, or that don't have the type of atmosphere you're looking for (in terms of company size, for example). One of the first steps in any job hunt is deciding what companies are likely to hire someone with your skills and experience and, of those companies, which ones you would like to work for. The easiest way to do this is to first sit down and think about what you want to do, and in what type of atmosphere you'd like to do it.

Decide what type of company you want to work for. Look at geographical location, product line, company size, and customer type (such as industrial or consumer). Try to figure out at which companies your skills can be best put to use, and what are the most commonly hired positions at these companies.

Researching Employers through Commercial Online Services

Services like America Online and CompuServe are gold mines of valuable information for job seekers. Job hunters can find detailed information that helps them target potential employers or prepare for job interviews. Costs of the services will vary. Most databases on CompuServe charge a search fee in addition to the CompuServe subscription charges. It typically costs around $45 to obtain full company profiles for five companies. America Online, on the other hand, has a smaller selection of business resources, but the information is available free of charge. Many job seekers may find they don't really need the in-depth financial information that many of the more expensive databases on CompuServe provide.

Researching Employers Online

The type of company information you can find online varies greatly, from the telephone book style of the Web's "Big Book" to the detailed financial reports found in Dun & Bradstreet's Business Reports through CompuServe. Some information comes in the form of employer databases like the CD-ROMs discussed in the next chapter, where you can conduct searches according to criteria such as geographic location and industry. Many Websites simply contain a list of companies, with links to each company's home page. General job hunting sites, like Monster.com, include employer profiles of those companies with job listings at the site (check out the listings in Chapter Four to find out which sites offer company profiles). Other databases, both on the Web and through commercial online services, contain much more in-depth information regarding a company's history, financial standing, or its products and services.

If you have a relatively short list of target companies you would like to learn more about, another option is to simply check out each company's home page on the Web. Companies of all sizes and in all industries are constantly developing an online presence. Since most sites are geared toward consumers, most individual company Websites include detailed information regarding the company's products and services. Others might include a company history; a list of company officers; financial information, such as historical stock performance or financial statements; and—of special interest to job hunters—employment information!

The Internet and commercial online services are also excellent resources for researching companies in periodicals. Today, most of the country's largest newspapers (including the *New York Times* and the *Wall Street Journal*), as well as magazines, trade publications, and regional business periodicals, have online versions of their publications. Many have their own Websites, or are available through a commercial online service like The Microsoft Network or America Online. If you are looking for information on a particular company, you can simply type in the company name, and search the publication for references to that company. Many publications even allow you to search their archives going back as many as three years (access can be restricted to subscribers).

The databases you choose to search will depend upon what information you are seeking. If you would simply like to find a list of all financial consulting firms in Chicago, a database like the Web's Big Book is probably adequate. But if you are preparing for a job interview as a high-level financial analyst, you need to have a solid grasp of the company's finances. You can easily gather that type of information through a service like Dun & Bradstreet.

You may often find that companies are listed in two or more databases. You may be tempted to simply disregard the additional information and move on to a company you don't have information about. However, it's wise to compare the information contained in the different databases. If the information is consistent, then it's probably safe to assume that it's correct; however, if the two sources conflict, you should try to find a third source to determine which information is correct. It's also likely that many databases will contain different information; one may have financial information, and another may have a list of the chief executives. You should also take care to watch the timeliness of the information you are finding; while most online databases are updated frequently, that is not always the case.

CompuServe is a commercial online service that has many excellent resources for researching both national and international companies. Usenet newsgroups, Bulletin Boards, or Gopher sites, though often extremely helpful in other areas of job hunting, generally contain little information that would be useful in researching companies and potential employers.

There are many advantages to researching companies online. The first is convenience; you can search right from your own home computer, instead of going to the library or employment service to use their information. Similarly, you can research companies whenever it's convenient for you–the Internet is available twenty-four hours a day. This convenience is especially valuable for last-minute job interviews. For instance, say you receive a call at three o'clock, asking you to come in for an interview the next morning. In the past, you might have panicked because you wouldn't have had adequate time for research. But with the Internet, the information is right at your fingertips (if you know where to find it). Also, the information on the Internet is generally kept up to date (though this is not always the case), with many companies updating their information daily, and some even hourly. Finally, researching companies can go much faster on the Internet. Once you know where to look, the information is only a few keystrokes away. You no longer have to carve out a large part of your day to go to the library and do research.

As for disadvantages, well, there really aren't that many. In most cases, accessing this information is free (except for your online monthly charges, of course). And while some services—especially those found only on commercial online services—charge for accessing some information, there's generally enough free information out there so that looking in fee-based databases is not always necessary. If you do have to enter a fee-based area, consider how valuable that knowledge is, especially for job interviews. One possible disadvantage involves updates. As we mentioned, some sites are updated quite often, but others receive little attention in this regard. In order to verify that you're getting current information from a site, look for when the site was last updated ("Last updated on June 7, 1999," or "This site updated on June, 7" or something to that effect) or for dates in articles or press releases at the site.

Researching Employers on the Web

New resources for researching potential employers are popping up regularly on the World Wide Web. To find additional resources, use a search engine like Yahoo! or AltaVista, and type in the keyword "companies" or "employers." You can also tap into job hunting Meta-lists, such as Purdue University's Center for Career Opportunities—Sites for Job Seekers and Employers (**http://www.cco.purdue.edu/student/jobsites.htm**), which provides links to numerous other career resources.

Listed below are several examples of databases that can be used to search for employers. These databases can be accessed free of charge, although there are several others that do charge small fees for searches.

Big Book
http://www.bigbook.com

While not specifically designed for job hunters, Big Book contains the names, addresses, and phone numbers of hundreds of thousands of businesses throughout the country. You can search the extensive database by category, business name, state, and city. Big Book can be tremendously useful for job interviews: by selecting a particular company in your targeted list, you'll see a detailed map of the area near the business, with the company's exact location highlighted (not available for all listings). Big Book also has a classifieds section with an employment section (through a link with http://www.classifieds2000.com).

EDGAR Database of Corporate Information
http://www.sec.gov/edgarhp.htm

EDGAR, or the Electronic Data Gathering, Analysis, and Retrieval system, is the electronic filing arm of the Securities and Exchange Commission (SEC). All publicly traded companies, and many others, are required by law to file certain documents with the SEC. Some international companies also file with EDGAR, but this is not mandatory. Job hunters can search the database for specific companies, and are likely to find information such as forms 10K and 10Q (annual and quarterly reports), as well as Form 144 (notice of proposed sale of securities) and other financial information.

Lexis-Nexis
http://www.lexis-nexis.com

Lexis-Nexis offers a variety of services which are available in books, on CD-ROM, through an online dial-up connection, and on the Web. Overall, the Lexis-Nexis database offers access to two billion documents and 8,700 individual databases, derived from nearly 25,000 sources. More than one and a half million subscribers conduct more than 400,000 searches on the service every day. The service offers information on industries (from aerospace to health care, and more) and professions (from financial analysts to journalist, and more). NEXIS is the part of the service that is responsible for developing and selling business, financial, and public records information to businesses and the government. NEXIS is the largest online service of its type, and offers comprehensive industry and company reports.

The following is a list of just a few of the general job hunting Websites that provide access to company profiles (please see Chapter Four for additional listings):

America's Employers
http://www.americasemployers.com

CareerCity
http://www.careercity.com

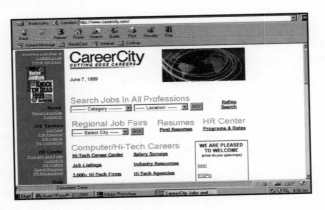

CareerMagazine
http://www.careermag.com

CareerMosaic
http://www.careermosaic.com

E-Span's JobOptions
http://www.espan.com

The Internet Job Source
http://www.statejobs.com

JobHunt
http://www.job-hunt.org

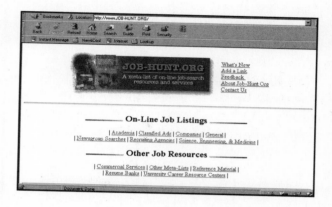

JobWeb
http://www.jobweb.com

Monster.com
http://www.monster.com

Philadelphia Online
http://www.phillynews.com

Searching for Company Websites

As mentioned earlier, a company's home page on the World Wide Web is often one of the best sources of information for job hunters. You can learn the company history and read the company's mission statement, which generally provides the names of its chief executives. Many sites for larger, public companies include information for stockholders, like financial statements, annual reports, earnings reports, and stock quotes. Many Websites also contain press releases where you can read about recent developments within the company, such as new product launches, changes among executives, or other important information.

The tone of a home page can also be a good way to get a feel for the company's corporate culture. For instance, Ben & Jerry's (**http://www.benjerry.com**) lighthearted depiction of cows and dancing skeletons is consistent with the laid-back, easy-going culture that the company promotes. Arthur Anderson's home page (**http://www.arthurandersen.com**), on the other hand, has a professionalism and polish that is appropriate for an international Big Six accounting firm.

For many job hunters, however, the most valuable information to be found on a home page is employment information. Many of this country's leading employers, from Adobe Systems, Inc. (**http://www.adobe.com**) to Wal-Mart (**http://www.wal-mart.com**), post job listings on their home pages. Home pages that don't contain job listings usually include some general information on how to apply for a job, such as a postal or email address. Others go into a little more detail, outlining requirements for some common positions and describing the departments within the company. In either case, this is usually more information than you can get from most employer databases, or from speaking to a human resources representative within a company.

In effect, looking at a company's Web page amounts to one-stop shopping for job hunters. Instead of calling companies for annual reports, searching through executive directories for the name of the second vice-president of marketing, and poring over old business periodicals looking for news regarding a potential employer, you can simply log on to the company's Web page and find this information. Of course, the content of each company's home page will vary—there is no uniformity to sites on the World Wide Web. Some sites have more information than you could possibly need, while others only skim the surface.

Unfortunately, you can't simply look up a company's URL in the telephone book like you can an address or telephone number. Luckily, however, you can use large Web search engines and directories to find the URLs of thousands of companies. The **Career Resource Center** (**http://www.careers.org**) is a good resource to start with. This Metalist of job hunting resources contains thousands of links to employers, job listings, reference materials, and more. You can either perform a broad search of all general Web directories, or browse through the more manageable category lists, such as technology companies or financial services. Companies include Ford Motor Company (**http://www2.ford.com**) and Digital Equipment (**http://www.digital.com**).

ELECTRONIC EMPLOYER DATABASES & CAREER SOFTWARE

Electronic employer databases have now made it possible to easily research potential employers. These databases, which are generally available on CD-ROM, can contain detailed information on up to *ten million* U.S. and international companies. Other databases include news articles from business and trade publications, or press releases and other material from individual companies. Electronic employer databases and career software provide job hunters with additional resources, allowing them to quickly search and isolate information that is crucial in an efficient, successful job search.

About Electronic Employer Databases

While most company directories are not specifically designed for job hunting, they contain a tremendous amount of valuable information for anyone looking for another job. Most directories will give you the same basic information, such as company name, description, address, phone and fax numbers, and number of employees. Virtually all directories will list one or more contacts, so you know exactly whom to call for information or where to send your resume. Others will also give you the name of the parent company or subsidiaries, email or home page address, product information, biographical information on key personnel, and financial information. Some directories are broad and include companies of all sizes and industries, while others are specialized according to industry, size, or company revenue.

Electronic employer databases offer a wide variety of search options. Standard & Poor's Register alone has fifty-five different search possibilities. The most basic are by geographic location or industry, so you can look for all the companies in your field that are located in your city or state. Other common search options are company size or revenue, SIC code (which stands for Standardized Industrial Code), or zip code. Some databases can be searched by job title, parent company name, stock symbol, or where key personnel went to undergraduate or graduate school. In the Martindale-Hubbell Law Directory, for instance, you could search for the names of all attorneys born in 1950 who went to Harvard Law School.

Employer databases can be especially helpful to job seekers considering relocation. You can find out, before you move, if you will realistically be able to find work once you get there. You can search for companies in virtually any region of the country, and you can get a head start on your job hunt by sending out resumes and cover letters before you move. Another big advantage of electronic employer databases is their timeliness. Most electronic database publishers release new versions of their databases more than once a year. Many even update their information monthly or quarterly, which means that you will always find up-to-date information concerning a company's address, phone number, key personnel, and financial condition.

Note: Before using an employer database, you should have a clear picture of the type of company you want to work for. While employer databases can be great tools for job hunters, they're virtually worthless if you have no idea what you want to do.

Since most of these databases can cost more than $500 and are designed for use by other businesses or libraries, don't expect to find these at your local software store. Of course, not all libraries will have all of these resources. Depending on how technologically advanced your library is, you may only find one or two of these electronic databases. Call your library to find out what electronic resources it has available. Many of these databases can also be found in the offices of career counselors or outplacement specialists, and are used as part of their service.

A Listing of Electronic Employer Databases

1999 American Big Businesses Directory
800-555-5211

Available through InfoUSA, the *1999 American Big Businesses Directory* provides profiles of 189,000 privately and publicly held companies employing over 100 people. The CD-ROM contains company descriptions which include company type, industry, products, and sales information. Also included are contact names for each company, with a total of over 645,000. You can search the database by industry, SIC code, sales volume, employee size, or zip code. Available only through libraries. **Note:** Information on the CD-ROM is formatted in all capital letters.

American Business Disc
800-555-5211

Also from the makers of the *1999 American Big Business Directory*, this CD-ROM is the most extensive, containing information on more than ten million U.S. companies. The profiles give you contact information, including contact name and title, as well as the industry and company size, in terms of both employee size and sales volume. The profiles also indicate whether a company is public or private, as well as detailed information regarding the company's products. There are a number of different search methods, including keyword searches by industry, SIC code, geographic area, or number of employees. Available only through libraries.

American Manufacturer's Directory
800-555-5211

Made by the same company that created *1999 American Big Business Directory* and *American Business Disc*, *American Manufacturer's Directory* lists over 622,000 manufacturing companies with 20 or more employees. The directory contains product and sales information, company size, and a key contact name for each company. The CD-ROM can be searched by region, SIC code, sales volume, employee size, or zip code. **Note:** The print directory lists 161,000 companies, and the CD-

ROM lists all 622,000 companies. However, the directory and disk are sold as a set. Available only through libraries.

CorpTech EXPLORE Database on CD-ROM

http://www.corptech.com

800-333-8036

Price: Ranges from $795 to $5,995

The CorpTech EXPLORE Database on CD-ROM contains detailed descriptions of more than 50,000 mostly private, technology companies. It also lists the names and titles of executives—CEOs, sales managers, R & D managers, and human resources professionals, so job seekers can contact the appropriate managers within a given company. You can also find home page and email addresses. In addition to contact information, job seekers can find detailed information about the products the companies make, services they provide, and their annual sales revenue. The CorpTech EXPLORE Database also provides an easy way to determine the growth of the company; it lists not only the number of current employees, but also the number of employees as of twelve months ago. Some companies also list the number of employees they expect to have in one year, so job seekers can see how much the company expects to grow. Job seekers can search the database using more than 33 different criteria, such as the type of company, location, or sales revenue. You can also create a more personalized search by entering criteria for all fields. The producers of this database provide free quarterly updates, and the database can be found in many public and university libraries.

D&B Million Dollar Database

http://www.dnbmdd.com

800-526-0651

Price: Ranges from $795 to $9,975

Operated by Dun & Bradstreet, this database lists information on more than 1.25 million companies. This is an expansive database, covering virtually every industry. The database tells you the number of employees, sales volume, name of the parent company, and the corporate headquarters or branch locations. Of special interest to the job seeker is the inclusion of the names and titles of top executives, as well as biographical information, including education and career background. Searches can be done by location, industry, SIC code, or executive biography. This database, which is updated every 60 days, can be found at many colleges and universities, as well as at some public libraries.

Gale Business Resources
800-877-GALE

Produced by the Gale Group, this database is geared more towards businesses than job hunters. However, you can still find plenty of valuable information within the database. The CD-ROM is compiled from *Ward's Business Directory*, *World's Business Directory*, and many other databases, and contains information on more than 448,000 companies worldwide. Job seekers can find contact names, number of employees, and type of industry. Also included is information on the company's products and revenue. The database can be searched by industry, company products, or geographic location.

Harris Database
http://www.harrisinfo.com/aboutdat.htm
800-888-5900
Price: Products range in price from $49 to $7,995

Produced by Harris InfoSource, this database of manufacturers profiles more than 360,000 companies. Although most companies are located in the United States, the database also provides listings for some companies overseas. Besides contact information, job seekers can find out the number of employees, plant size, and sales revenue. Updated annually, the directory is available in CD-ROM format, and can be found in libraries, universities, or the offices of executive recruiters. The directory is also available in smaller regional or state editions.

Hoover's Company Capsules on CD-ROM
http://www.hoovers.com/hoov/store/electronic_frame.html
512-454-7778
Price: $499.95

Published by Hoover's, Inc., Hoover's Company Capsules on CD-ROM gives in-depth profiles of more than 11,000 companies and 30,000 executives. The in-depth corporate profiles include detailed information on the company history, products, and growth prospects. The profiles also include information taken from the company's financial statements. The industry profiles include information on industry averages and projected growth for the industry. Updated quarterly, Hoover's Company Capsules on CD-ROM can be found at most public and university libraries.

JobBank List Service

800/872-5627 (or in MA: 781/767-8100)

email: jobbank@adamsonline.com

A compilation of company information derived from the *JobBank* series of career directories. This database of private and public companies nationwide is frequently updated to ensure the most current information and high degree of accuracy. Company information is provided in ASCII comma-quote-delimited text format either by e-mail or on disk. Each order is quickly compiled according to criteria determined through a consultation (by phone or email) between a *JobBank* editor and the customer. There is no minimum order. Criteria for companies or employment agencies can be specified geographically, by industry, by occupation, or any variation/combination desired by the customer.

Martindale-Hubbell Law Directory on CD-ROM

http://www.martindale.com/products/law_dir_cd.html

800-323-3288

Price: N/A

As the name indicates, this is a directory consisting exclusively of the names of legal employers. In all, the database has listings for over 900,000 lawyers and law firms. In addition to information regarding firms and practices, the database includes the biographies of many individual lawyers who are also listed. Thus, you can do searches using more than 20 criteria, including area of practice, firm name, law school attended, and field of law. While it does list international law firms, the database consists primarily of U.S. firms. This CD-ROM database is available to job seekers in most law libraries, as well as some university and public libraries.

Moody's Company Data

http://www.fisonline.com

800-342-5647

Price: N/A

Moody's Company Data is a CD-ROM that has detailed listings for over 10,000 leading publicly traded companies. In addition to information such as industry, company address, or phone and fax numbers, each listing includes the names and titles of top officers, including the CEO, president, and vice president, company size, number of shareholders, a corporate history, subsidiaries, and financial statements. Job seekers can conduct searches by region, SIC code, industry, or earnings. Updated monthly, this CD-ROM is available at public and university libraries, as well as the offices of some outplacement specialists.

Standard & Poor's Compustat Research Insight (North America)

http://www.compustat.com/products/univ_mkt.htm
800-221-5277
Price: $79/semester, or $129/year (for students at schools with a network subscription)

The database lists thousands of top international companies and up to 20 years of market history for those companies. The database (North America) also offers similar information for 1,000 Canadian companies. Research Insight (North America) also offers the names of company officers, monthly stock prices and business descriptions for thousands of companies, and basic data, such as SIC codes, company names and addresses, type of business, locations, and more. There is also Research Insight (Global) which offers the same type of information for 10,000 companies in more than 60 countries. Other Compustat products include Annual Back Data on CD-ROM, which offers company information dating back to 1950; and ExecuComp for Windows, which offers information on compensation for more than 12,500 top executives. You'll find this database available through university libraries.

Researching a Company for a Job Interview

Once you have scheduled an interview with a targeted company, you will need to begin your in-depth research. In order to prepare yourself for an interview, you need to know the company's products, types of customers, subsidiaries, parent company, corporate headquarters or regional locations, rank in the industry, sales and profit trends, whether the company is publicly or privately held, and current plans. You need to find out everything you can about the industry, the firm's principal competitors and their relative performance, and the direction in which the industry and its leaders are headed.

While many electronic employer databases will give you much of this information, you also need to take your research a step further. Reading relevant articles about the company or the industry will enable you to enter your interview with more confidence. Plus, the interviewer will be impressed if you are able to speak intelligently about industry trends or about the company's future plans.

But unless you are interviewing with a high profile company like Nike or Microsoft, company and industry news can be hard to find. This is especially true if you have an interview in a distant city or state, where you are less likely to have access to local information. **Business periodical databases** can contain hundreds of thousands of articles on business and industry. Most contain either full articles or abstracts (summaries) from hundreds of national, regional, and local business publications. From these articles, you can learn about what products a company is developing, marketing strategies, personnel moves, and financial condition—all the information you should know for an interview. You can also find articles dating back one or two years, which allows you to track the performance of a particular company over time. Other databases contain financial statements, Securities and Exchange Commission filings, or press releases from individual companies.

Like electronic employer databases, you can search business periodical databases in a number of ways: by company name, industry, region, or topic. Conducting a topic or industry search can often be a way to learn valuable information about a company's market share and competitors. By simply pressing a few keys, you can get a wealth of information—articles, press releases, and industry reports—about a company or industry.

Look for business periodical databases at your local public library, including the example detailed below. Again, not every library will have every database. Call to determine what resources are available, or to find out where you can get these resources. Most colleges and university libraries carry them as well.

Investext®
http://www.investext.com/Investext/analysis/invest.htm
800-662-7878

The Investext database is a valuable resource for job hunters searching for detailed financial information about a particular company. Job hunters can use the database to analyze a company's line of business, locate current and historical financial information, or perform competitive analysis on products and companies. The database contains financial and business reports on more than 10,000 U.S.companies (provided by Moody's Financial Information Services). The reports are compiled by 500 leading Wall Street, regional, and international brokerage, investment bank, and research firms.

Job Hunting and Resume Software

Job hunting software is yet another electronic advance that has helped take some of the mystery out of looking for a new job. Like most software products, job hunting programs have made the job hunting process easier than ever before. While these programs can't go out and find a job for you, they can help you create more polished, professional-quality resumes and cover letters, organize your contacts and job leads, and prepare you for job interviews. All of this can make you a more attractive candidate for any employer who looks for these characteristics—professionalism, organization, and preparation—in potential employees. What's more, many packages also include job hunting tips on everything from networking to what you should wear to a job interview. Some programs even have sections on assessing your career, which helps you figure out what jobs are best suited for you based on your personality, experience, and preferences.

Whether or not you decide to invest in one of these software packages will largely depend on your individual needs. Do you simply want to write your resume, or do you want help with other areas of job hunting, such as finding out what questions you are likely to be asked during a job interview? And if you simply want to create a new resume, what kind of word processing software do you own? Many word processing programs already contain several different styles of resumes on templates. If you only want to change the format of your existing resume—or you want to create a new resume and you already have a good idea of what to say and how to say it—then you can probably make do with your current word processing software.

If, on the other hand, you want to write a brand-new resume, but you're not sure where to begin, job hunting software can help. The software can walk you through each step of the resume writing process, and provide you with features such as prewritten phrases or samples on which to base your resume. Similarly, resume writing software allows you to create customized cover letters or other business correspondence with ease. Most resume writing programs include many of the same features commonly found in word processing software, such as a spell-checker, thesaurus, mail merge, and envelope printing. Some also have a feature that automatically condenses a resume onto a single page if it spills over to a second page.

Another advantage of resume writing software is the flexibility it offers. For instance, you can easily try out different formats to see which is most appropriate for your resume—usually with a simple click of a button on a toolbar. Or, you can create multiple resumes with various formats or objectives tailored for use with different companies or job openings. For instance, you could have one resume focusing on one set of skills and another emphasizing other experiences or skills.

However, the best part of job hunting software is the fact that these programs are far more than just glorified word processors. Most programs include a contact manager, a section on job interviewing, general job hunting advice, as well as other special features, such as a database of potential employers. The contact manager is often the most basic part of the software—it is essentially a database where you can enter information on contacts, job leads, potential employers, or other notes that could be helpful to discuss in a job interview. Most also come with a calendar function that allows you to schedule and keep track of events such as phone calls made, letters sent out, and job interviews.

The sections on job interviewing are often the most impressive part of the software. Most of these products come in CD-ROM versions, and the multimedia capabilities of that medium really bring these sections to life. You can actually see and hear interview questions, and listen to sample answers and tips on how to answer the questions. The packages feature advice from top experts in the job hunting and career development field. These experts give you the answers to dozens—and in some cases, hundreds—of questions you may encounter in a job interview. You also learn why each question is asked, and get advice on the do's and don'ts of responding to the questions. Depending on the program, you can also listen to expert advice on writing resumes and cover letters, or about the job hunt in general.

Again, not every job hunter needs all of the features found in these products. For instance, if you are by nature very organized and a good record keeper, then you probably don't need another source to manage your job hunt. Also, the sample interview questions and answers discussed in these job hunting packages are not much different than those found in the leading books on job interviewing. Similarly, you can find most of the same general job hunting advice given within the pages of any of the dozens of books on job hunting that can be found at your local bookstore. At the same time, this type of software can be invaluable to someone who simply doesn't know where to begin his search, or whose job search is in need of a jump-start. In particular, the sections on resumes and cover letters can help revive a tired old resume, and the nature of the multimedia CD-ROM makes the job hunting tips and interviewing advice more lively and engaging.

When looking at job hunting software packages, you'll notice that most products have the same basic components—resume writing capabilities, a multimedia section on interviewing, and a contact management program. Also, there's not a large price differential between products. However, some products emphasize one area more than another, such as resumes or interviewing, while others offer special features, like employer databases or access to the Internet. Unfortunately, as Macintosh owners are well aware, there is usually less of a selection to choose from when it comes to buying software—or any other computer accessories—for a Macintosh, and job hunting software is no different. However, while most software is available only for Windows, many of the leading resume software packages also come in versions for Macintosh.

It's worth noting that software companies frequently release new and updated versions of their products. Therefore, while the features described on the following pages are accurate at the time of this writing, there can be no assurances that these will be the features available by the time you read this. Similarly, retail prices may vary slightly according to individual stores or region, and prices are subject to change by the manufacturer. That said, the following are a few examples to get you started in creating your new resume.

Adams Almanacs on Disk and CD-ROM

System Requirements: 486 or higher PC-compatible computer; Windows 3.1 or higher, including Windows 95 and Windows 98; 2 MB RAM (4 MB for CD-ROM); 3.2 MB free hard disk space (5 MB for CD-ROM); double speed CD-ROM drive (for CD-ROM only); sound blaster or compatible audio; mouse; 256 color VGA (SVGA recommended).
Manufacturer's Price: $19.95 each
Adams Media Corporation, 800-USA-JOBS

Adams Cover Letter Almanac & Disk

This package includes a print almanac and an accompanying floppy disk. The software includes a choice of dynamic opening sentences, effective following paragraphs, and sure-fire closings; a complete word processing program; and a tutorial that shows you how to make a terrific cover letter.

Adams Resume Almanac & Disk

This package includes a print almanac and an accompanying floppy disk. The software includes a full range of resume styles and formats; ready-to-use action phrases that highlight your skills and experience; a tutorial that shows you how to make an effective resume; and a full word processor with ready-make layout styles.

Adams Job Interview Almanac & CD-ROM

This package includes a print directory and an accompanying CD-ROM. The CD-ROM features more than 300 video and 200 audio clips to guide you through an interview. Decide how many questions you want to answer and go one-on-one with one of the world's top experts on job interviewing.

ResumeMaker™ Deluxe Edition on CD-Rom

System Requirements: 486 Pentium PC-compatible or higher; Windows 95/98/NT or later; 8 MB RAM; double speed CD-ROM drive or higher;, sound card; 256 colors VGA adapter or higher; speakers or headphones; at least 20 MB hard disk space; an additional 12 MB hard disk space for the Career Planner.
Retail Price: $39.95
Individual Software, 800-331-3313

ResumeMaker Deluxe CD is more than just resume writing software; it's a complete guide to career planning and job hunting. Guided Resumes and Letters take you through each step of the resume writing process to create professional-looking resumes and cover letters. In the resume section, you can choose from chronological, functional, or focused formats. From there, you simply fill in the appropriate information for each section. The focused resume option gives you suggestions for writing a resume tailored for different fields and situations, including technical, publishing, or recent college graduates. The guided cover letter includes prewritten paragraphs for each of four types of letters; again, you simply fill in the blanks with your personal information. The virtual interview section tells you what questions you are likely to be asked in an interview, along with sample answers and the "rationale" behind each question and answer. The program also tells you what questions you should ask in an interview, as well as what questions you might be asked that are illegal. But the software encourages people to plan a career, not simply get a job. The software also includes a detailed Career Planner, a program designed to help you find your ideal career. By answering dozens of questions in each of three areas—work values and environment, experience and interests, and abilities—the program creates a personalized profile of your work preferences. Based on your profile, the program generates a "Personal Career List" of possible careers. And since this system is not always perfect, you can continually modify your answers to come up with a revised list of potential careers.

WinWay® Resume 6.0

System Requirements: 486SX PC-compatible or higher; Windows 3.1 or Windows 95/98/NT or later; 12 MB free hard disk space; CD-ROM drive; sound card.
Retail Price: $39.95
WinWay, 800-4-WINWAY

This comprehensive resume and job hunting software package contains sections on creating resumes and cover letters, managing contacts, and job interviews. The resume and cover letter sections include thousands of samples that cover several different fields and job titles. The resumes also cover a variety of different career situations, including military personnel entering civilian life, frequent job changers, and recent grads. A special feature of the resume and cover letter sections is the AutoWriter function. For resumes, you can either fill in your personal information for the resume to format, or choose from more than 100,000 keywords and phrases to insert into your resume. Similarly, AutoWriter will supply you with prewritten paragraphs for a number of different types of letters, including ad response, networking, or interview follow-up letters. The Contact Manager has fields for name, company name, and notes, as well as additional space for more detailed information about the company, such as annual sales revenue or history. The interview section contains advice, answers, and tips for hundreds of interview questions. It even includes sections on how to answer stressful or "off the wall" questions. What's more, the program lets you skip around so you can look only at the area of questioning you're interested in. The program includes some additional features, including: a mail-merge function; email that converts your resume to either ASCII, RTF, or HTML; a Salary and Benefits Guide; and job hunting strategies to follow before, during, and after the interview.

CHAPTER EIGHT

NETWORKING
ONLINE

Ask anyone in the employment industry—consultants, outplacement specialists, human resources professionals—and they will probably tell you that the best way to find a job is through networking. In fact, one common figure tossed around employment circles is that eighty percent of all jobs are found through networking. Not by contacting employers directly, not through employment agencies, and not through the newspaper help-wanted ads. Therefore, establishing a solid, extensive network of contacts within your field of interest should be a top priority.

While some may think that top executives and industry insiders are the only people to benefit from networking, that is not the case. The development of specialized online discussion groups has made it easier for all job hunters to meet and interact with other professionals in the same field or industry. Every day, thousands of job hunters log on to the Internet's Usenet discussion groups or mailing lists, or visit the special interest groups (SIGs) on commercial online services in order to discuss issues and developments relevant to the field, compare experiences, or exchange information, including employment opportunities.

Usenet discussion groups, mailing lists, and SIGs are ideal for networking since they were designed so that people interested in the same things could discuss their similar interests by posting and reading messages. Today, there are hundreds of online discussion groups on virtually any topic, ranging from religion to politics to popular TV shows. The dozens of career-related discussion groups available cover fields like accounting, education, journalism, and microbiology.

The main objective of networking is to become visible to prospective employers. Other benefits of online networking include:

- **Discussion group participants often include human resources representatives and hiring managers,** who often lend their expertise by discussing the qualities they look for in employees. And, many recruiters report visiting field-specific discussion groups to look for potential job candidates.
- **Participating in online discussion groups brings far greater exposure than, for instance, going to a meeting of a local industry group.** A discussion group's audience is most often nationwide, and may even include participants from around the world.
- **Monitoring discussion groups makes it easy to determine what skills and experiences employers are looking for.** For instance, do most of the other participants have their MBAs? It's also a good way to find out which companies are hiring and what are the hot topics and issues in the field.

Job hunters should look at three main areas as potential networking resources: Usenet newsgroups, mailing lists, and special interest groups on commercial online services. Gopher and the World Wide Web do not lend themselves well to networking since they were not designed for two-way communication. Newsgroups, mailing lists, and SIGs, on the other hand, were designed expressly for the purpose of disseminating and receiving information. At the same time, keep an eye out for Websites of industry organizations and associations. While they do not have the ability to accept posted messages, field-specific Websites are still a good way to keep up with the latest developments and advances in a particular field, and to keep abreast of the hot issues in that field.

Do not expect to be besieged with job offers and contact names simply because you logged on to a professional discussion group and posted a message full of intelligence and insight. Networking online is a slow process, since in the online world, just as in real life, relationships do not form overnight, and it takes time to build up trusted contacts. In fact, it may be months before any job leads materialize. That's why we suggest continually maintaining a presence in appropriate discussion groups—even when you are happily employed—since the opportunity of a lifetime may turn up when it's least expected.

The Importance of Netiquette

"Netiquette" is simply a combination of the words "network" (or Internet) and "etiquette." Originally used to describe the rules surrounding Usenet newsgroups, netiquette now refers to the widely accepted do's and don'ts for using any type of online discussion group. It is essential that new users, or "newbies," are familiar with the netiquette of a group before joining the discussion; otherwise, they might get "flamed" (criticized and ridiculed by established group members).

The easiest way to avoid getting flamed is to spend time observing and reading the group's posted messages *before* attempting to join the discussion. Each discussion group, especially those on Usenet, have a particular tone and rules. Simply "lurking" (reading messages but not posting your own) in a particular group will give you a good sense of the group's personality. This is also a good way to ensure that a particular group will really fit your interests.

When you are ready to join in the discussion, don't simply post a general message along the lines of, "Hi, I'm new here and just wanted to drop in and say hello!" Post a message asking for specific advice, or introduce an original thought or comment to the discussion. A boring, generic posting with headers like "Help!" or "Hire Me!" will be ignored at best, and will get you flamed at worst. If you do get flamed—something that is bound to happen to every new user once or twice—just ignore it. Unless you violated a sacred rule of netiquette, someone was probably just having a bad day.

Following are some other basic rules of netiquette, as well as some general guidelines to follow in professional discussion groups:

- **In all postings, write in full and complete sentences,** and be sure that all spelling, punctuation, grammar, and capitalization are correct.
- **Don't type messages in all capital letters** because that's the online equivalent of SHOUTING.

- **Don't use "emoticons" such as** :) (happy face), or : ((frown), or common abbreviations like BTW (By The Way) and IMHO (In My Humble Opinion) which are commonly used in recreational discussion groups. These types of cutesy short-hand are out of place in a professional discussion group, and if you want to be taken seriously, don't use them.

- **Understand the appropriate times to post or email a reply to a particular message.** Many new and experienced users alike are often unsure of when to direct an email to the message's author, and when a reply should be posted to the group. In general, post a reply if your message is something the group as a whole could appreciate and learn from, but use email if your comment only concerns the author. This is important because no one wants to participate in a discussion that is little more than a dialogue between two or three people.

- **Finally, use your best manners.** Respect and be tolerant of others' ideas and opinions.

Networking on Usenet Newsgroups

Newsgroups are a terrific place for networking, with discussion groups to suit almost every interest. Newsgroups also tend to have the harshest rules of netiquette, due in part to the fact that—since newsgroups are one of the oldest areas of the Internet—their participants are more technologically savvy than the online world as a whole. At the same time, their users are extremely knowledgeable, and helpful to those who have taken the time to learn the rules. *Please see Chapter Three for a list of newsgroups.*

Networking with Mailing Lists

Mailing lists, also known as list-serves or email discussion groups, are like a cousin to Usenet discussion groups. Like newsgroups, mailing lists allow users to post and read messages that contain threads of discussions on various topics. What sets mailing lists apart from newsgroups is that instead of users logging in to a specific group and posting and reading messages online, subscribers automatically receive new messages, and post messages to the group, via email. Many users like mailing lists because they allow users to monitor discussion groups simply by checking their email, which is something many of us do everyday.

To subscribe to a mailing list, send an email to the list's system administrator. The list administrator makes sure that all messages are sent to subscribers, and moderates the content, ensuring that postings are relevant to the topic. Like other discussion groups, each mailing list has its own rules and guidelines, so be sure to contact the list's administrator for details.

There are tens of thousands of mailing lists available, covering subjects like arts, business, health, politics, and religion. To find the mailing lists that match your interests, consult the selection of online directories that follow. Each directory contains contact information, such as the system administrator's email address, for over 50,000 mailing lists.

Liszt, The Mailing List Directory
http://www.liszt.com
This directory claims to be the largest directory of mailing lists, and it just may be, with more than 90,000 lists available for searching. The site also allows you to search by keywords.

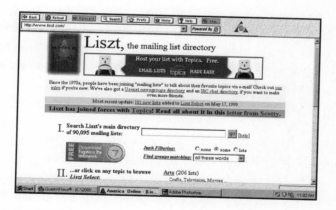

Publicly Accessible Mailing Lists
http://www.neosoft.com/internet/paml
This list is searchable by name, subject, or keyword. It contains hundreds of different subject classifications. Check under "jobs" or "employment" for job-related mailing lists, but check out lists in your field as well. This list is also posted to the Usenet newsgroups **news.lists.misc** and **news.answers** around the end of each month.

Special Interest Groups (SIGs)

SIGs are found only on commercial online services, such as America Online and CompuServe. SIGs, like newsgroups, are a means by which people with similar interests can gather online to exchange ideas and information. While these groups are called different names on each service—forums, bulletin boards (*not to be confused with the Bulletin Board Systems discussed in Chapter Five*), roundtables—they are known collectively as SIGs.

SIGs differ from newsgroups in a number of ways. First, SIGs have smaller audiences, because fewer people subscribe to commercial online services than have access to the Internet. Also, most SIGs have moderators, called sysops, or system operators, who monitor the discussions to be sure that the comments are relevant to the specific group. They also make sure that the discussions don't get out of hand, which despite netiquette, can occasionally happen (this is usually called a flame war). And in most special interest groups, the main subject is subdivided into smaller directories, which make it easy to pinpoint the exact topic you want to discuss.

Finally, keep in mind that the commercial online services provide their subscribers with full Internet access. Therefore, if they don't offer a forum that fits your interests, browse the newsgroups and mailing lists directories for a group that seems more appropriate.

Commercial Online Services

America Online
In addition to America Online's outstanding career resources, the service also has a number of forums for networking with other professionals. AOL's forums, listed in Chapter Two, offer other valuable information in addition to their message boards. To find a complete list

of America Online special interest groups, search for the keywords "clubs" and "forums" in the Directory of Services.

CompuServe

With over 700 forums, CompuServe has by far the most discussion groups for professionals, with forums in a wide range of fields. CompuServe is well-known for the quality of its forums and the participants therein. Its forums have three basic components: the message section, where users can post and read messages; conference areas that allow users to participate in real-time chats, as well as scheduled meetings or conferences with other users; and libraries, which enable users to search for archival information such as conference transcripts and articles related to the forum's topic. Most forums require you to join them, but there is no fee for membership. Often, forums may restrict access to nonmembers; in some forums, for instance, you may not have access to the libraries or conference rooms if you have not joined.

CHAPTER NINE

COMPUTERIZED INTERVIEWS AND ASSESSMENT TESTS

Just when you thought the whole job search process couldn't get any more high-tech, along comes the computerized job interview. Many companies, especially those that regularly hire large numbers of employees, are now having candidates complete a computerized job interview in place of an initial screening interview with a human resources representative. Like the traditional screening interview, the computer asks the candidates questions regarding their work history, background, skills, and qualifications, usually in the true/false or multiple choice formats. Once the interview is complete, the computer provides the interviewer with a summary of the candidate's answers. Among other things, this summary might recommend bringing the candidate in for a face-to-face interview, and provide the interviewer with a list of follow-up questions for the second interview.

Candidates who have taken computer-assisted interviews give high marks to the computer; many report being less anxious and nervous during the interview. Human resources professionals like the system because it streamlines the hiring process and makes it more efficient. Companies that use computer-assisted job interviews report higher productivity, improved customer service, lower employee turnover and absenteeism, and less theft in the workplace.

Computerized job interviews are based on the principle of the structured job interview. Structured job interviews, which have long been valued by human resources professionals, are simply interviews where the same prescribed set of questions are asked of every candidate applying for positions within a company. (Of course, this is usually only used for the initial screening interviews; second interviews generally tend to be less structured and more of a conversation.) Advocates of the structured interview say that it brings a consistency and fairness to the hiring process that is lacking when nonstructured interviews are used. The standardized format of the interview allows recruiters to more easily compare candidates' responses—each candidate gets asked the same question phrased exactly the same way. Also, each question is carefully phrased so the interviewer doesn't have to worry about breaking any employment laws. One final advantage—structured interviews gather more information in less time than nonstructured interviews.

Brooks Mitchell, Ph.D., founder, and president of SHL Aspen Tree Software and a leader in the field of computer-assisted job interviews, was the first person to see how easily a computer could perform the initial screening interview. After all, he reasoned, what could be more consistent and impartial than a computer? Mitchell based his idea on the structured job interview, and in 1978, administered the first computer-assisted job interview in a large New Jersey plant. Since then, the use of computer-assisted interviews has continued to grow in fields and companies that traditionally hire large volumes of workers, such as banks, hospitals, hotels, and retailers. These types of companies can have hundreds of entry-level job openings each year, and since employers typically interview as many as ten candidates for a single position, the computer-assisted interview can greatly increase the efficiency of the hiring process. Since the computer screens out any unqualified candidates, the hiring manager spends time only with those candidates who have the skills and qualifications necessary for the job.

What to Expect from a Computer-Assisted Job Interview

A computer-assisted job interview proceeds in much the same way traditional job interviews do, except your interviewer is a piece of expensive machinery. You get called for an interview, schedule a mutually convenient time to meet, come into the office, and meet with a human resources representative. However, instead of the traditional screening interview, you will be led to a computer workstation, where you will be given instructions on how to take the computer-assisted job interview.

Most interview programs are intuitive and, providing you are computer-literate, easy to navigate. You are generally given a time limit, usually about thirty minutes, in which to finish the interview.

Expect to be asked about one hundred questions regarding your educational background, employment history, job skills, work ethic, and more. Here is an example of some questions you might expect from the ApView computer-assisted interview from SHL Aspen Tree Software:

1. Are you currently employed?

   A. Yes
   B. No

2. Why did you leave your last job, or why do you want to leave your present job?

   A. I was dismissed
   B. I was laid off
   C. To take a better job
   D. Relocation
   E. To go to school
   F. I am not leaving my present job
   G. Other reason

3. How often do/did you experience conflict with your co-workers?

   A. Often
   B. Sometimes
   C. Rarely
   D. Never
   E. Cannot say

4. What kind of recommendation do you think your present or most recent supervisor would give you?

A. Outstanding
B. Above average
C. Average
D. Below average
E. I don't know

5. At previous jobs, were you able to develop new or better ways of doing the work assigned to you?

A. Most of the time
B. Usually
C. Sometimes
D. Seldom
E. Never

In the past, most computerized job interviews consisted entirely of multiple choice or true/false questions, but now some computerized interview systems contain a number of questions that require more extended, written responses. ApView, for example, offers its customer companies the option of using open-ended questions instead of, or in addition to, multiple-choice questions. Naturally, these types of answers are reviewed by a recruiter or hiring manager, not a computer. Most computer-assisted interviews are custom-made for each company or position. Generally, the interview is developed to address specific issues for a given position or family of positions. This eliminates the possibility that you will be asked questions that are irrelevant to the position for which you are applying.

You should answer the questions in a computer-assisted job interview just as you would in a traditional job interview. Don't exaggerate your skills and accomplishments. For instance, don't tell a computer you have five years' experience in retail if, in reality, you only have experience as a seasoned shopper. Remember, a computer-assisted interview is only the first step; if you get selected for a face-to-face interview, the interviewer will see from your application and resume that you were lying to the computer, which will virtually eliminate you from contention.

What's more, it's important to be more accurate with computerized interviews because, unlike their human counterparts, computers will immediately pick up on any inconsistencies in your responses. A human interviewer may be too distracted to pick up on any contradictions during an interview, but a computer is programmed to flag inconsistencies for the interviewer to discuss in your follow-up interview.

What the Computer Tells the Interviewer

Once you have completed the interview, the recruiter will explain to you the next steps in the interviewing process. Generally, the program will analyze your responses and present a summary to the recruiter. The recruiter will read the report and then decide whether you have the qualifications that would warrant a second interview. Among other things, the report summarizes basic background information, like education level and length of employment with your past or current company. It will also highlight those questions where you had an abnormally long pause before responding. This is done because several studies have shown that it takes longer to lie than to tell the truth. The report also flags inconsistencies and contradictions in your responses. For instance, some systems may have tricks worked in, so if you gave a certain response to a particular question or set of questions, the computer will flag those responses for the recruiter. Most programs will also provide the recruiter with a list of follow-up questions that is based on your answers to the computerized interview. For instance, in the sample questions listed earlier, the follow-up to question number five is, "Give me an example of something you developed on a previous job that enhanced a work assignment."

Some programs will also compare the results of your interview with a standardized employee profile that has been developed for a particular company. By comparing your answers with those of successful hires, the computer can predict—usually with measurable success—whether you will be a successful employee.

Note: A computer never makes the final hiring decision. It simply presents a report to an individual recruiter, and it is up to this individual to analyze the data provided and determine whether or not to invite a candidate in for a second interview. So don't worry about your fate being in the hands of a machine; for better or worse, the final decision is still left up to a real person.

Why Employers Like Computer-Assisted Job Interviews

SHL Aspen Tree Software, the makers of the ApView interview system, reports that employers like computer-assisted job interviews because they ensure that each candidate is thoroughly and—most importantly—impartially screened. With computer-assisted interviews, the information gathered is more accurate and reliable. What's more, advocates of these systems believe that the selectivity of the computer screens out borderline candidates who may have otherwise advanced, thus improving the overall quality of employees. One company reported a 33 percent lower turnover rate in the first six months of using a computer-assisted interview for the initial screening interview. Some other advantages of the computer-assisted job interview include:

- avoids traditional interviewing problems, such as forgetting to ask important questions or letting personal feelings interfere with the interview
- gathers more information about a candidate in one-third the time it would take a human interviewer
- information is more accurate—applicants are more likely to be honest with a computer

Companies also often use computerized interviews for situations where accuracy and honesty are essential, such as exit interviews, in-house promotion interviews, or to measure employee morale and attitude. Since people are generally more honest with a computer, companies can get a more accurate reading of their employees.

How Computer-Assisted Job Interviews Can Help You

By now you might believe that the computerized job interview is another step towards the depersonalization of the workplace by a corporate America that's increasingly beginning to resemble "Big Brother."

But you should be aware that the computerized job interview offers job hunters several important benefits.

The biggest benefit is probably the same reason you might balk at the prospect of sitting down for an interview with a computer: it's impersonal, unfeeling, and unsympathetic. Thus, with a computer, you are freed from the biases that, to some extent, every human interviewer possesses. A computer won't be judgmental or prejudiced—it won't have preconceptions based on your gender, race, height, weight, clothes, or voice. In short, computers are objective interviewers. A computer will never—consciously or subconsciously—allow personal feelings and biases to cloud its assessment of a candidate.

Computers are also less intimidating. A computer can't lead you to answer in a particular way, either verbally or through body language. Similarly, a computer won't react after you answer a question—no raised eyebrows, cringes, or even smiles. Since you aren't receiving any feedback, you can feel free to answer honestly, instead of giving an answer you think the interviewer wants to hear. Remember, however, that a real person will be reviewing your answers from the computer interview, so don't answer computer-assisted questions any differently than you would questions posed during a traditional interview.

A computer-assisted job interview also helps to keep the playing field level. Often, a less qualified applicant will advance ahead of a more qualified applicant, solely because the less qualified applicant happens to have a stronger personality. However, with a computer-assisted interview, you can be assured that you are judged on your skills alone. Personality still plays a strong role in the interview process, yet when computer-assisted interviews are used, an applicant's personality may become a factor during subsequent face-to-face interviews.

Finally, you can also be assured that the computer will be concentrating 100 percent on you and your interview. A computer won't be thinking about an overdue project, a critical meeting later in the day, or what it's going to have for lunch. Also, you don't have to worry about encountering a computer that is simply having a bad day.

Of course, a computer-assisted job interview still has a few major shortcomings. First, some people say that the questions in these programs are biased against certain groups, especially women and minorities. Also, a computer is not always able to take into account certain special circumstances, such as a history of unemployment because of a disability or family obligations, and will thus provide a negative report to a recruiter. Finally, a computer is not, obviously, a person. A computer is not able to discern the intangibles that make us who we are—it cannot measure eagerness and enthusiasm, or alternatively, negativity and pessimism. So while a computer is generally more efficient than a person, it can never fully replace the human touch in the hiring process.

Computerized Applicant Screening by Telephone

Job interviews via the telephone are nothing new to job hunting. The telephone interview is often the first contact a job hunter has with a potential employer: a human resources person or hiring manager will call a candidate, ask a few basic questions, and, if those questions are answered satisfactorily, invite the candidate in for a face-to-face interview.

A computerized telephone interview is really no different from a regular telephone interview. It's designed to get a better sense of a candidate's background to help determine suitability for a particular position. SHL Aspen Tree Software and Pinkerton Services Group are just two of the companies that create this type of telephone interview. With the ApView interview from SHL Aspen Tree Software, an applicant calls a phone number and—using a touch-tone phone—answers some basic questions regarding his or her qualifications for a particular position. If the candidate meets the position's requirements, then the candidate can simply schedule, over the telephone, a more in-depth interview. SHL Aspen Tree reports that this system is especially helpful to companies that are planning to hire workers in large numbers, such as for site openings or seasonal employment.

Pinkerton Services Group designs computerized structured interviews for client companies. Offered as part of their pre-employment assessment services, the IntelliView Structured Interview System is a 100-question interview about an applicant's employment background. These questions are of the yes/no variety, which makes it easier on the applicants because they have less information to remember before they respond. This system, which can be administered either over the telephone or on a computer, is generally not custom-made for a particular company or position, but rather, the industry in general. Each interview contains about 100 generic questions regarding a specific industry, such as retail, health care, child care, or work area, such as customer service. For instance, someone taking the child care interview may be asked if he or she likes to work in an orderly, quiet environment. If the candidate answers yes, then this person probably would not last long working in a daycare center.

Most of the advantages of the telephone interview are similar to those for the computer-assisted interview. They save a company time by efficiently screening out unqualified applicants, and can help improve the overall quality of employees. For instance, an unqualified applicant won't get by because he "sounded nice." For job applicants, the process is free from bias, so they can answer questions honestly and accurately. Furthermore, you don't have to worry about being put on hold while the interviewer tends to an urgent matter in the office.

The disadvantages of the computerized telephone interview are also similar to those of the computer-assisted interview. These types of interviews lack the personal touch that is sometimes a crucial element in the interview process, and they may not allow an applicant to fully emphasize his or her strengths early on.

The Internet Job Interview

This method of interviewing is quickly gaining popularity, especially for long-distance job hunting. For instance, say you're applying for a position with a company in Chicago, but you live in San Francisco. If you are hooked up online, you can simply complete a screening interview on your own home computer—instead of paying for an expensive flight and hotel room. Again, the process starts like any other: you are contacted for an initial screening interview, but instead of scheduling an initial telephone or face-to-face interview, you are provided with a password that gives you access to the company's in-house computer system. Once you log on, the process is essentially like that of a computer-assisted job interview. You are asked basic questions about your background and work experience, and the computer generates a report for the recruiter. Again, companies like this method because it's a big time-saver, but it is also beneficial to job hunters, since travel expenses for job interviews are usually paid for only the most high-level executives, or most highly sought college recruits.

Scenario-based Job Interviews

Like the name implies, scenario-based interviews involve more situational interviewing than the structured, computerized multiple choice interviews that were discussed in earlier sections. These types of systems are used to see how candidates will behave in simulated, real-life work situations. Learning Systems Sciences, a leader in this type of computerized interview, reports that their clientele consists primarily of banks and retail establishments, including many large department store chains. Like the structured, computerized job interviews, these interviews are most often used to screen candidates for entry-level positions that traditionally have high turnover rates. If candidates pass these simulations, they will be brought in for a face-to-face interview.

John King, vice-president of Learning Systems Sciences, reports that many companies prefer this type of interviewing because instead of simply asking someone, for instance, how they feel about customer service, the employer can actually see how a candidate will perform in tough situations. For instance, the computer screen might show an irate customer yelling about a product he bought that he believes is faulty, and the candidate must try to placate the customer.

Instead of simply keying in one of a set of preformulated answers, the computer actually records the voice of a candidate, thus allowing the recruiter to hear how the candidate handled the situation. Did the candidate remain calm and polite, or did the voice sound harried and rude? Candidates are usually graded on a decided-upon scale. For instance, a candidate might get extra points for apologizing to a customer, but could get points taken away if his or her voice didn't sound sincere.

Since these types of systems actually assess how well someone can read a particular situation and act appropriately, companies that use them report lower turnover rates than those that still use traditional methods. Like users of the computerized, structured job interviews, companies that use these systems also report an improvement in the overall quality of employees.

Computerized Assessment Tests

Assessment tests are nothing new to the world of job hunting. For years, job applicants have been asked to take all kinds of tests to evaluate their suitability for a job. The reasoning behind these tests is simple: hiring new employees is time-consuming and expensive. By carefully screening applicants with both structured, computer-assisted job interviews and computerized assessment tests, recruiters can greatly reduce the chances that a new hire will leave after only a few short months, and consequently, the time and expense of another candidate search will be avoided.

Employers generally use three main types of assessment tests: skills, integrity, and personality. The purposes of each of these tests are pretty basic: skills tests determine if you have the ability to do a particular job; integrity tests help determine whether you will be a trustworthy employee; and personality tests tell the interviewer if your disposition is suited for a particular position. Depending upon the nature of the position you are applying for, you may be asked to take one, two, or all three of these tests. Most positions require some type of skills test, for example a math test for accountants and a typing test for administrative assistants. Some computer programmers are even asked to write a short program as part of their pre-employment testing. If you are applying for a position where you'll be dealing with goods or money, you will probably be required to take an integrity test. Personality or psychological tests can be used in virtually any situation, but are especially common if you are interviewing for a management position or one where you would be working with sensitive material.

Pinkerton, the well-known security and investigation firm, stresses that prevention—by using pre-employment screening such as personality and integrity testing—is the best way to reduce or eliminate serious workplace issues such as theft, drug use, or even employee violence. To this end, Pinkerton has created a number of automated integrity, personality, and skills tests, including the Stanton Profile, the Stanton Survey, and the Adult Personality Survey.

What to Expect from a Computerized Assessment Test

Computerized assessment tests are generally administered after the initial screening interview, while skills tests can often be part of the initial screening process. However, personality and integrity tests are usually given as one of the last steps of the interviewing process. If you are asked to take a computerized assessment test, your interviewer will likely lead you to a semi-private or private room with a computer. After you receive instructions on how to use the program, the test will be administered, usually within a specified time limit. Depending on the nature of the test, you may simply answer multiple choice or true/false questions, or you may transcribe written information into a specific computer program. Integrity and personality tests typically contain upwards of 100 questions. Most are of the multiple choice, yes/no, true/false, always/sometimes/never variety. When your time is up, the computer will score your work, and, if applicable, compare your answers to a specified profile. The computer then generates a report for the interviewer to review. It should be made clear that the computer doesn't actually tell the employer whether someone should or should not be hired; it simply tells the recruiter how a candidate fits in relation to other candidates.

Computerized Skills Tests

Skills tests are the most straightforward types of computerized assessment tests. Basically, they measure your aptitude for performing a specific task or duty. Anyone who has done any temporary work will be familiar with many computerized skills tests. These tests simply determine your proficiency in various word processing, spreadsheet, and database programs. With these computerized programs, you are asked to do some basic exercises using the various applications, and you are tested on your accuracy. With some tests, especially those for word processing programs, you will have a certain amount of time to—for example—format and write a document. Then the computer will not only test your accuracy, but also how much you managed to accomplish in that time. Similarly, a spreadsheet test might judge you on how quickly and accurately you can enter data and perform different functions on the spreadsheet.

Again, computerized skills tests cover all fields. An accountant or engineer may be tested on their mathematical or logical reasoning skills. A computer programmer might need to write a few lines of code or debug a problematic program. Or you may be asked to take a test that measures reaction time, or that tests your memory. With computerized skills tests, anything is possible.

Computerized skills assessment tests are measured on your raw score. Your score is then measured against a mean, or average score of everyone who has taken the test. For instance, if you scored a seventy-five, and the mean is sixty-eight, that will show the employer that you have above-average skills. Unfortunately, there's no real way to prepare for skills tests. The best you can do is prepare for the type of test, such as a typing or math test, that is likely to be administered during a job interview by brushing up on those skills.

Computerized Integrity Tests

Integrity tests, such as Pinkerton's Stanton Profile, are another type of computerized assessment test. Basically, these tests measure your honesty and morals. The Stanton Survey, for instance, is designed to measure the moral standard by which you live. By moral standard, this doesn't just mean whether someone is likely to embezzle company funds or steal from the cash register. An applicant's level of honesty and moral standard can also help determine whether someone is likely to be tardy, socialize excessively during work hours, leave early, take long lunches, "borrow" office equipment, and so forth.

Integrity tests allow employers to measure the reliability, work ethic, and trustworthiness of a candidate. These traits are all important indicators of a candidate's future performance. For instance, a recruiter might question the candidacy of an applicant who, on his integrity test, stated that it's all right to steal sometimes.

When taking an integrity test, try to avoid absolutes, like always or never. No one is likely to believe you if you say you have never in your whole life lied, or you have never gotten so much as a parking ticket. Simply be honest, but don't reveal more than you have to.

Computerized Personality Tests

Personality tests are the most complex of all computerized assessment tests. These are generally used to test a candidate's personal make-up to see if his or her personality is suited for a particular job. Tests such as Pinkerton's Adult Personality Survey measure specific personality traits such as work motivation, adaptability, and trustworthiness. The results of a personality test are then compared against a standard, or norm, group which has been developed from all who have previously taken the test. For instance, if you are applying for a position as an insurance underwriter, your scores will be measured against a norm group of successful underwriters.

Companies like personality tests because they allow companies to see if you will "fit in" with the company and the position. This is beneficial to both you and the employer, because if you are ultimately not happy with your job, it hurts both you and the company. The company has wasted time and money to train you only to have you quit in a few months, while you have wasted time in a job that ultimately didn't make you happy.

Another Pinkerton test is the Stanton Profile, a hybrid personality/skills test that measures general employability. This test measures your work preferences; your score is measured against the minimum requirements of a particular job. For instance, the test will ask you a question regarding your adaptability, a good trait for someone applying for a position as an administrative assistant, but not for someone working in a stockroom, since that person will likely be doing the same tasks day after day with little variation.

While preparing for skills and integrity tests is difficult, preparing for personality tests is nearly impossible. First of all, many people aren't sure if they should let their "true" selves answer questions, or if they should answer questions based on the kind of personality they think the company is looking for. Experts differ on the subject. Some suggest you use your work personality, while others say you should just be yourself. Still others suggest coming up with a "character" based on successful friends and colleagues.

We suggest you look at what's helped you get where you are, and also what has held you back. If you have spent any time in the work force, you should realize that your work personality differs from your personality outside of work. Therefore, it is best to use what you have learned in the workplace—what is and is not acceptable workplace behavior to answer the questions. If you are new to the workplace, this logic still applies. Look at what traits and strengths have worked for you and brought success in the past, and focus on those.

And as with the integrity tests, try to avoid using absolutes like "always" and "never." A large number of always and never answers might make it look like you are lying, or worse, be a signal of extreme behavior. Employers typically favor candidates with moderate behavior, as opposed to those indicating extreme behavior.

GLOSSARY
OF
TERMS

ASCII (ass-key): An abbreviation for American Standard Code for Information Interchange. It is the most basic code for written documents (such as resumes or letters) that all computers understand. ASCII files contain no special formatting, like italics or boldface. It was invented to enable different types of computers to communicate with each other. It's often referred to as DOS text or plain text.

Access: The ability to connect to a service or resource and receive information. Accessing certain services may require special software (as with commercial online services) or registration (as with Bulletin Board Systems).

Address: The combination of letters and/or numbers that enables you to reach another computer or user online. People with online/Internet accounts have email addresses where they receive their email. A fictional example of an address is, **yourname@computer.com**. On the Internet, the address is also called a URL.

BPS: BPS stands for bits per second, and it is the measurement of how quickly a modem can send and receive information via telephone lines. The slower your BPS, the longer it takes to receive information online. At the time of this writing, 56,600 BPS modems are the standard.

Baud: The scientific unit of measurement for data transmission speed. Usually measured as one bit per second. Not to be confused with BPS, which is the correct term for measuring modem speeds.

Bookmark: To store a site's Web page address, thereby eliminating the need to type in a URL every time you want to return to a particular site. This feature is found on most Web browsers.

Bulletin Board System: Commonly abbreviated as BBS, a Bulletin Board System is like a mini-online service, catering to communities or to particular interests. Basically, it's a computer set up with communications software, a modem, and one or more phone lines. It's an easy way for users to meet, exchange information, and find computer files and software. Many BBSs also offer their users some form of Internet access.

Click: To select an element, either some text or an image that appears on the computer screen, usually by pressing on the mouse button (once or twice, depending on the application) and cause another action to happen. For instance, on the Web, if you click once on underlined words, you will be transported to another document, file, or directory on the Web. If you click twice on an icon on your desktop, you will open that program.

Clients: Special programs that retrieve information from other computers and computer networks, called "servers."

Commercial online service: A service that charges a fee for access to its online resources that were developed especially for the use of its subscribers. These services usually charge extra for access to particular services, such as databases or newspapers. The most popular commercial online services include America Online, CompuServe, and The Microsoft Network.

Communications software: The software that enables you to use your modem. Communications software controls the exchange of information between your modem and a remote modem.

Computer-assisted job interview: A job interview administered by a computer. It's designed to take the place of the traditional screening interview, and usually consists of multiple choice and true/false questions about a candidate's employment history and background.

Computerized assessment tests: Tests administered by a computer that help determine job fit. Computerized assessment tests usually fall into one of three categories: skills, personality, or integrity.

Cyberspace: A general term often used when referring to the Internet and other online services. It's also used when discussing computers in general.

Database: A large, organized collection of information that's stored electronically. A database's carefully constructed design enables users to search for and locate specific information—such as job listings in a particular field or location—quickly and easily.

Discussion group: An electronic meeting place for people with shared interests to chat, discuss ideas and issues, and exchange information through the posting and reading of messages. It's the general term used when referring to Usenet newsgroups, mailing lists, or special interest groups on commercial online services.

Download: To transfer data (such as files) from another computer to your own.

Electronic resume: A traditional resume that's stripped of most of its formatting so that it can be easily read and searched by a computer.

Email: Email, or electronic mail, is a standard service that comes with most communications software, Internet connections, and commercial online services. It allows you to send and receive messages through your computer.

FAQ: Frequently asked questions. Compilation of questions (along with their answers) that are most commonly asked. Posted by most newsgroups, mailing lists, special interest groups, and other online services for the benefit of new or inexperienced users.

Forum: A specific name for special interest groups or discussion groups found on CompuServe, America Online, and Delphi, where participants can post and read messages regarding specific topics.

Freeware: Public domain software files that are available to users free of charge.

Gopher: Often referred to as the grandparent technology of the Web, Gopher is a menu-based system that easily allows users to explore all areas of the Internet, usually with the help of Gopher's search engines, Jughead and Veronica.

HTML: Hypertext markup language, the text formatting language that makes use of hypertext and is used to write documents on the World Wide Web.

Home page: Home pages are usually maintained by companies, organizations, the government, educational institutions, and even individuals. The home page is also referred to as the first page of a Web site, where you can find, for example, the main menu of options.

Hypertext: Hypertext enables users to jump from one page to another to access information, such as text, graphics, or music, through predefined links. It's the concept upon which the World Wide Web is based.

Internet: The global network of computers that transmits information via telephone lines, enabling computers from all over the world to communicate with each other. It's used by many different organizations, such as educational, commercial, and government institutions, to convey news, entertainment, and other information to users worldwide. It's also the general term used when referring to Gopher, Telnet, Usenet, and the World Wide Web.

Jughead: The smaller of the two main search engines for Gopher, the other being Veronica.

Keyword: A word or short phrase that is used to search a database of documents or files. When filed, documents, such as resumes, are indexed using a particular set of words that refer to key concepts within that document. When you perform a keyword search, the computer searches all documents and files within a particular database (or databases) for matches between the keyword and one of the indexed words.

Link: Created using hypertext, links are what connect you to a different site on the World Wide Web. The new connection may be with a different Web page or simply a file or subdirectory within a large site or down the same page. Links are most often represented by underlined words, though some may be presented as graphics.

Log in: Often "log on." To connect with a remote computer or computer network, such as a commercial online service or BBS.

Mailing list: Also known as list serve. A type of discussion group found on the Internet, in which users send and receive messages through email.

Meta-list: A "list of lists" found on the World Wide Web with links to Websites and other Internet resources on a particular subject, such as job hunting. These lists are good time-savers since they generally include a short description or review of the site or service, so you won't waste time visiting irrelevant or low-quality sites. Plus, to access a particular site, you only need to click on the site name.

Modem: From MOdulator/DEModulator. A communication device that converts data from computers into sound that is transmittable via a telephone line, thereby allowing remote computers to communicate with each other through ordinary phone lines. Information is now being transferred more and more via cable lines, as well.

Multimedia: The joint use of several different forms of media, such as text, sound, graphics, and video in a single application, such as a Web page or CD-ROM.

Netiquette: The established set of manners used when participating in Usenet newsgroups and other online discussion groups. It's important to be familiar with the netiquette of a particular newsgroup before jumping into the discussion. Created from combining the words "network" or "Internet," and "etiquette."

Network: Computers that are physically connected, usually through hardware, to facilitate the sharing of information. There are two basic kinds of networks: Local Area Networks (LANs), which are relatively close together, in the same office, for instance; and Wide Area Networks (WANs) in which the computers are scattered across cities, states, or countries. Technically, the Internet is considered a Wide Area Network.

Newsgroup: The name of online discussion groups found in Usenet. These electronic message boards are by far the most popular type of discussion group.

Online: To be linked via modem to another computer or computer network. To say that you're "online" generally means you are connected to a Bulletin Board System, the Internet, or a commercial service like CompuServe.

Post: Post, or posting, is used as both a noun and verb. As a noun, a post is what you may find and read online, such as job listings or a message in a newsgroup. As a verb, post is when you send a message or a document (like a resume) to a BBS, newsgroup, special interest group or even a Website.

Protocol: The set of rules that determine how different computers exchange information. For instance, the documents in the Web address **http://www.yahoo.com** must be retrieved using hypertext ("http" stands for hypertext transfer protocol).

Search engine: An information or database retrieval tool that enables users to quickly and easily search the vast amounts of information found on the World Wide Web (some may also search Usenet). Two examples of search engines are Yahoo! and Excite.

Server: A main computer or computer network that relays information when "asked" by special software called "clients."

Shareware: Software files that are available free to users for a limited time only, called an "evaluation" period. After the evaluation period, you must pay in order to use the software.

Site: A specific place on a commercial online service or the Internet (including the World Wide Web) where users can find information.

Special interest group: The type of discussion groups found on commercial online services. Includes bulletin boards and forums.

Telnet: A way of connecting to a remote computer or network over the Internet. You navigate Telnet by using command line prompts. It's also a *type* of Internet site that you may connect to. For example, you can Telnet directly to a Telnet site, or Telnet to a Gopher server.

Thread: A string of related messages on the same topic found in Usenet newsgroups and other discussion groups. It contains both original posts and replies to those posts.

URL: Short for Uniform Resource Locator. It's the uniquely identifiable address for any Website—such as a file, directory, or other computer—on the World Wide Web. For instance, **http://www.whitehouse.gov** is the URL for the office of the President of the United States.

Upload: To transfer data (such as files) from your own computer to another computer.

Usenet: Abbreviation of User's Network. This is a vast, international network of more than 20,000 different online discussion groups on practically every topic imaginable. Usenet is only one part of the Internet, and was created specifically to allow users to exchange news and other information.

Veronica: The largest search engine for Gopher. Acronym for "Very Easy Rodent-Oriented Netwide Index to Computerized Archives."

Web browser: Software, such as Netscape Navigator, that enables users to navigate the World Wide Web. It "reads" the hypertext documents on the Web, including text, intricate layouts, and graphics, and presents them to the end users.

World Wide Web: The part of the Internet that uses hypertext links and graphics to convey all kinds of information—news, entertainment, and more. The hypertext links enable users to easily jump between different documents and files, thus making exploring the Internet both simple and fun. Commonly referred to as the Web.

INDEX

-P, Q-

-R-

-S-

Your Job Hunt
Your Feedback

Comments, questions, or suggestions? We want to hear from you. Please complete this questionnaire and mail or fax it to:

The Adams Electronic Job Search Almanac
260 Center Street
Holbrook, MA 02343. U.S.A.
Fax: 781/767-2055

You may also email your responses to **jobbank@adamsonline.com**.

Did this book provide helpful advice and valuable information which you used in your job search? Was the information easy to access?

Recommendations for improvements. How could we improve this book to help in your job search? No suggestion is too small or too large.

Would you recommend this book to a friend beginning a job hunt?

Name: _____

Occupation: _____

Address: _____

Daytime phone: _____

Email address: _____

JobBank List Service
Custom-Designed For Your Job Search

Generated by the same editors who bring you the nationally renowned JobBank series, the electronic JobBank List Service is a compilation of company information that is important to you. Our huge database is updated year-round to ensure that our data is as accurate as possible. Our company information is available to you by e-mail or on disk in ASCII delimited text format.

Whether you're looking for a small company to work for, or a large corporation to do business with, JobBank List Service can help! JobBank List Service is not mass-produced for the general public; it is built for you through a personal consultation with a member of the JobBank staff.

While other services offer their company information on pre-generated disk or CD-ROM, we construct the data explicitly to match your criteria. Your JobBank consultant will work with you to find the company information that applies to your specific job search needs. Criteria for companies or employment agencies can be specified geographically, by industry, by occupation, or any variation or combination you can imagine ... you decide.

With the most current information on companies in more than thirty industries, jobseekers, recruiters, and businesses alike will find the JobBank List Service the perfect solution to their personal and professional needs. Industries covered include:

- Accounting and Management Consulting
- Advertising, Marketing, and Public Relations
- Aerospace
- Apparel, Fashion & Textiles
- Architecture, Construction, and Engineering
- Arts, Entertainment, Sports, & Recreation
- Automotive
- Banking/Savings and Loans
- Biotechnology, Pharmaceutical & Scientific R&D
- Charities and Social Services
- Chemicals/Rubber & Plastics

- Communications: Telecommunications & Broadcasting
- Computer Hardware, Software, and Services
- Educational Services
- Electronic/Industrial Electrical Equipment
- Environmental & Waste Management Services
- Fabricated/Primary Metals & Products
- Financial Services
- Food & Beverages/Agriculture
- Government
- Health Care: Services, Equipment & Products

- Hotels & Restaurants
- Insurance
- Manufacturing
- Mining/Gas/Petroleum/Energy Related
- Paper & Wood Products
- Printing and Publishing
- Real Estate
- Retail
- Stone, Glass, Clay, and Concrete Products
- Transportation
- Utilities
- Miscellaneous Wholesaling and many others

No Minimum Order – No Order is Too Small!
Thousands of Private & Public Companies in All 50 States & DC
Thousands of Employment Services
Each Listing Includes the Same Type of Detailed Contact & Business Information Offered in the JobBank Book Series
Standing Order Discounts are Available

Contact the JobBank staff now for your individual consultation and pricing information.
E-mail: jobbank@adamsonline.com
Phone: 800/872-5627 x5304 (in MA: 781/767-8100 x5304)
Fax: 781/767-2055

The Everything Get-A-Job Book
by Steven Graber
Managing Editor of the JobBank Series

*T*he *Everything Get-A-Job Book* gives you the competitive edge, with a fun and non-intimidating approach to looking for your first job or just plain trying to find a better job. Jammed with tons of tips, strategies, and advice from the trenches, this comprehensive book will be indispensible to anyone hoping to land a great job. Find out how to:

◆ Find companies that are hiring without picking up the want ads
◆ Uncover valuable networking opportunities
◆ Search in-depth for job openings on the Internet
◆ Extensive information on writing cover letters and resumes— including what not to do
◆ Prepare for evil interview questions
◆ Dealing with head hunters and employment services
◆ Strategies to land multiple job offers
◆ Negotiate the best salary, bonus, and benefits package
◆ And much, much more!

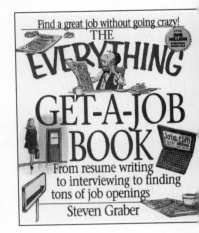

Find a great job without going crazy!

THE EVERYTHING GET-A-JOB BOOK

Jobs.com

From resume writing to interviewing to finding tons of job openings

Steven Graber

Trade paperback, 1-58062-223-2, $12.95
8" x 9¼", 304 pages

The JobBank Series

There are now 35 *JobBank* titles, each providing extensive, up-to-date employment information on hundreds of the largest employers in each job market. The #1 best-selling series of employment directories, the *JobBank* series has been recommended as an excellent place to begin your job search by the *New York Times*, the *Los Angeles Times*, the *Boston Globe*, and the *Chicago Tribune*. *JobBank* books have been used by millions of people to find jobs.

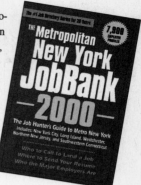

Each *JobBank* book is 6" x 9¼",
over 300 pages, paperback, $16.95.

- *The Atlanta JobBank*
- *The Austin/San Antonio JobBank*
- *The Boston JobBank*
- *The Carolina JobBank*
- *The Chicago JobBank*
- *The Connecticut JobBank*
- *The Dallas-Fort Worth JobBank*
- *The Denver JobBank*
- *The Detroit JobBank*
- *The Florida JobBank*
- *The Houston JobBank*
- *The Indiana JobBank*
- *The Las Vegas JobBank*
- *The Los Angeles JobBank*
- *The Minneapolis-St. Paul JobBank*
- *The Missouri JobBank*
- *The Northern New England JobBank*
- *The New Jersey JobBank*

- *The New Mexico JobBank*
- *The Metropolitan New York JobBank*
- *The Upstate New York JobBank*
- *The Ohio JobBank*
- *The Greater Philadelphia JobBank*
- *The Phoenix JobBank*
- *The Pittsburgh JobBank*
- *The Portland JobBank*
- *The Salt Lake City JobBank*
- *The San Francisco Bay Area JobBank*
- *The Seattle JobBank*
- *The Tennessee JobBank*
- *The Virginia JobBank*
- *The Metropolitan Washington DC JobBank*
- *The Wisconsin JobBank*
- *The JobBank Guide to Computer & High-Tech Companies ($17.95)*
- *The JobBank Guide to Health Care Companies*

If you are interested in variations of this information in electronic format for sales or job search mailings, please call 800-872-5627 x 5304, or e-mail us at jobbank@adamsonline.com.

Visit our exciting job and career site at http://www.careercity.com

From the publishers of the *JobBank* and *Knock'em Dead* books

Visit our Web Site: www.careercity.com

...free access to tens of thousands of current job openings plus the most comprehensive career info on the web today!

- ◆ Current job listings at top employers in all professions
- ◆ Descriptions and hot links to 27,000 major US employers
- ◆ Free resume posting gets noticed by top hiring companies
- ◆ Access to thousands of executive search firms and agencies
- ◆ Comprehensive salary surveys
- ◆ Directories of associations and other industry resources
- ◆ Hundreds of articles on getting started, changing careers, job interviews, resumes, cover letters and more

---

Post your resume at CareerCity and have the job offers come to you

It's fast, free and easy to post your resume at CareerCity—and you'll get noticed by hundreds of leading employers in all fields.